March 2003

To Nara /Ma~
Wishing you a
Day & Joyful re~
All our love
Suzy, And~

tie

xx &r

CU00406135

the WriteStuff!

POET

EAST LONDON

Edited by Clare Tupholme

First published in Great Britain in 2003 by
YOUNG WRITERS
Remus House,
Coltsfoot Drive,
Peterborough, PE2 9JX
Telephone (01733) 890066

All Rights Reserved

Copyright Contributors 2003

HB ISBN 0 75434 267 0
SB ISBN 0 75434 268 9

FOREWORD

This year, the Young Writers' The Write Stuff! competition proudly presents a showcase of the best poetic talent from over 40,000 up-and-coming writers nationwide.

Young Writers was established in 1991 and we are still successful, even in today's modern world, in promoting and encouraging the reading and writing of poetry.

The thought, effort, imagination and hard work put into each poem impressed us all, and once again, the task of selecting poems was a difficult one, but nevertheless, an enjoyable experience.

We hope you are as pleased as we are with the final selection and that you and your family continue to be entertained with *The Write Stuff! East London* for many years to come.

CONTENTS

Max Buadi	79
Phoba Mbuli	80
Leon Diamond	80
Kemelia Horne	81
Whitney Johnson-Yeboah	82
Charlotte Desimone & Lianne Cawley	82
Joel Adebayo	83

Chingford School

Risha Parmar	84
Sanna Saeed	84
Jo Southwell-Sander	85
Laura Goode	85
Stephanie Hughes	86
Blake Lewis	86
James Wright	86
Rochelle Harp	87
Maria Constantinou	87
Matthew Gregory	88
Jordan Wilson	88

City Of London School

Samuel Landau	89
Daniel Ong	90

Clapton Girls' Technology College

Maryam Khazaei	90
Susan Roberts	91
Andrée Wohi	91
Sameena Desai	92
Nazma Begum Ali	93
Tasneem Mithawala	94
Mumina Begum	94
Sharon Ogunbiyi	94
Ebru Buyukgul	95
Bunmi Odubanjo	96
Ruhie Dyer	97
Raj-Rani Kaur	98

The Poems

COUSINS

Cousins are very special, especially my cousins,
they are cousins everyone would wish for.
They shine like a star with no fear or shame,
they are caring, comforting and full of love.
Their hearts are made up of gold - so solid and never breaks.
They are such lovely cousins that I can hold and look up to.
The thing I love about them is they are all in one
full of qualities and never end,
but best of all they are my best friends.
They are also the answer to all my prayers.
When I'm sad and feeling low,
they are always there telling me to give it a go.
They would also be a heart if they were in the body,
but if they were anything they'd be everything!

Emma Kabir (14)

THE TELLY ADDICT

My grandfather is a telly addict
He watches it all day, all night.
My grandfather is a telly addict,
He watches the horror movies, until he goes white.

My grandfather is a telly addict,
He even has his very own TV schedule.
My grandfather is a telly addict,
He watches it so well I think he should get a medal!

My grandfather is a telly addict,
He concentrates so hard without a sound.
My grandfather is a telly addict,
He has no other information in his head to be found.

Lola Betiku (14)
Cardinal Pole RC School

It's a Goal!

I nteresting
I glanced at the ball and ran for it. I booted the ball and scored.
T errific
The crowd was amazed! Even I was amazed! Then cheered.
S o funny, (a bit)
So everyone praised me and loved me.

A ll footie style
All the newspapers had my name in them.

G ot to read this
God, I felt like a multimillionaire with everything I wanted.
O ne of the best
Oh I wish it could happen to me all of the time.
A crostic
All my life, I have been waiting for this moment. Ahh!
L aughter
Last game - I wished that it would happened again, but obviously
not this time, maybe next time.

Bernadette Adewale (12)
Cardinal Pole RC School

Shaded

I saw you with her again yesterday,
Acting so loving and caring.
So caught up in one another,
You didn't notice me standing and staring.

I called you earlier today,
To invite you out; you happily agreed.
You just called me and cancelled,
To ask why, there is no need.

Your love for her shines like the sun,
While I'm left in the shade.
The relationship I thought we had
Is slowly starting to fade.

But there is one thing in this mess
That you will have to accept.
I'm your daughter as much as she is,
And Dad, I've earned your respect.

Barbara Robertson (15)
Cardinal Pole RC School

BUSTED

Busted are my favourite band,
There's no one better throughout the land.
There's Mattie, James and Charlie too,
Three great guys I wish I knew.
'Britney' is a really cool song,
So is 'Sleeping With The Light On'.
'Psycho Girl' is quite sad,
James is a great writer, as well as a great lad.
Mattie sings great in 'Everything I Knew',
His padlock necklace and great hair are cool too.
Charlie is the youngest there,
And has cool all-over-the-place hair.
Their cool guitars and great style,
One look at them, you can't help but smile.
With a bit of Charlie, James and Mattie-Jay,
The Busted guys are here to *stay!*

Joanne Stapley (15)
Cardinal Pole RC School

FABIEN FLIES AWAY

F ive minutes before the game is over
A lan Smith crosses the ball in and Harry Kewell scores,
B arthez starts to cry and wishes he could fly away
I an Harte has been in a coma for 20 minutes.
E lland Road erupts
N asty Roy Keane has just been sent off.

F abien Barthez is now crying loudly
L uckily Ian Harte has just woken up from his coma
I nfact he's on the ball!
E ven Sir Alex Ferguson hopes they win
S mack! The ball has just broken the camera.

A way Barthez goes, he has just flown away,
W e have just heard Beckham is in goal!
A nd Beckham is playing well.
Y es Leeds have just won the game, thanks to Harry Kewell.

Ross Frew (12)
Cardinal Pole RC School

FABIEN

(The Number One Goalkeeper)

F lexible Fabien Barthez is very flexible, usually.
A wareness: he is aware of his surroundings.
B all: Fabien Barthez has a ball named after him.
I magination: Fabien Barthez is very imaginative.
E avesdropping, he always hears what his opponent's strategy is.
N early always wandering out of his goal.

Samson Osun (12)
Cardinal Pole RC School

BLACK VS WHITE

Black Vs white, who will win the fight?
It's a bad sight when they have a fight
In my dream, black people rap and white people clap.
I wish that could happen for real
Because when black and white have a fight
It gives me the chills.

White Vs black, who will win the fight?
When I am playing in the rain, black and white have a fight
And they are feeling the pain.
Sometimes I wonder if they would ever stop
And I wish they all could dance the hip pop.

Black Vs white, who will win the fight?
When I am up high, I am near to the sky
And I hate when they fight, it's a terrible sight.

Albert K Quartey & Damien Feeney (13)
Cardinal Pole RC School

HAPPY HOUR

H   appy is what it seems to be
A   nd it looks good
P   ersonally I'm tired of getting the kids ready for breakfast
P   laying is what they want to do, rather than go to school
Y   ou may think they're good, but they are terrors.

H   appily they have gone to school
O   h honestly! They are a handful.
U   p to now all they've done is argued
R   eading the news is what is on the television.

Reece Sammie Paul (12)
Cardinal Pole RC School

DIZZY

Everywhere I look I see different colours in my head,
I look at people I hate and all I see is red.
I look at all their funky clothes,
I just stand there and freeze.
People with blue and yellow hair.
Look at my socks, they're not a matching pair.
Wanting to get out right now,
Smell over there, it smells like a cow.
Maybe if I pinch myself.
Why oh why am I on a shelf?
Feeling like a book where no one looked.
Please, oh please, someone help me,
I'm gonna go mad at the count of 3.

Jermaine Smith (12)
Cardinal Pole RC School

NO LIFE

'Mum can I play football?'
    'No!'

'Mum can I have new trainers?'
    'No!'

'Mum can I have a burger!'
    'No! Fat is bad.'

'Mum can I have fifty pounds?'
    'No!'

'I understand Mum . . .
The teenager is dead and the adult is alive.'

Mencey Morera (14)
Cardinal Pole RC School

SCHOOL AND STREETS

People working, people fighting, mayhem all about
No people care as the head teacher stares.
I love it when class Vs class fight
It might just be a fight to the death, stupid faces, stupid noises
As the teacher turns round
To hear the beat of the sound.

As it is raining, people getting a beatin'
The fight still goes on
A drug dealer gives a ten-year-old boy a con

The battle still goes on
Between the streets and the school.

Joseph Hickey & Danio Lee (12)
Cardinal Pole RC School

THE NICE ONE

T he man is good, he scored his fifth goal today
H e cries like a baby on the ground
E yes are red because of the shock.

'N ice goal! It's the best!'
I said
'C an we see it again?'
E yes are happy because of the goal.

O ne man's score of the year and he will
N ever score again
E yes go red again because he will never do it again.

Darryl Paul (12)
Cardinal Pole RC School

LEG BREAKING LIMBO

L izzy! I hear
E veryone shouting out
G o girl! Do it for me.

B reaking bones, I feel all over
R eady for the whistle to blow.
E veryone is clapping for me
A ngry as I am already,
K eys jiggling, people wanting to go home
I knew they were just here for a laugh
N othing can stop me, I'm
G oing to do it.

L ong before this day
I knew I was going to do it.
M um pushing me on
B ut now I have accomplished it
O nly I had faith, and yes I've done it!

Stephanie Radford (12)
Cardinal Pole RC School

DOUGHNUTS

Oh my beautiful, fat, juicy doughnut
Fatter to me than the world
You're sugary sweet
You're more sugary than my feet
There's no other one like you
I love you too
You're fat, you're small
You're bigger than a ball
There's no other one like you.

Kike Ojo (13)
Cardinal Pole RC School

UNTITLED

F   abien is crying
O   h no, Fabien fumbles again
O   h yes, Kewell scores again
T   ip-toch, it's a goal
B   ing, bong, he's on a floor again
A   hrrrrah!
L   anky Larry misses again
L   ong lost goal.

F   abien is running again
A   t a great half-time
B   ing, bong oh no
I   t's a yellow card
A   great club lost
N   early but not near enough.

Raymond Smullen (12)
Cardinal Pole RC School

LIMBO DOWN

L   imbo down she goes
I   n a flexible and relaxed way
M   oves calmly and slowly and she enjoys it
B   ecause her aim is for gold!
O   nly she wants to be the best.

D   on't even mess
O   r lose the gold.
W   in it! Win it! echoes in her mind
N   o! Don't ever lose. No!

Christina Brown (12)
Cardinal Pole RC School

Oh Baby, Baby Girl

Oh baby, baby girl, I wish you were with me,
So that I could hold your hand and gaze into your eyes,
Oh baby girl, I wish you were with me.

When I first met you I would cry and cry and cry,
I thought you would reject me,
But then I tried and tried,
We talked for a while,
Then we realised we liked each other, girl.

Oh baby, baby girl, I wish you were with me,
So that I could hold your hand and gaze into your eyes,
Oh baby girl, I wish you were with me.

The next day I saw you I gazed into your eyes,
I told you I loved you
Then I held your hand.
I asked you to be mine, then you said, 'I will.'

Oh baby, baby girl, I wish you were with me,
So that I could hold your hand and gaze into your eyes,
Oh baby girl, I wish you were with me.

Everything was fine, but then he came along,
He ripped my heart out,
For that he stole you from me.

Oh baby, baby girl, I wish you were with me,
So that I could hold your hand and gaze into your eyes,
Oh baby girl, I wish you were with me.

I was so broken-hearted,
I cried and cried like the first time I met you,
Why, oh why did you do this to me?

I know now how it feels,
To be let down by a loved one,
How could you do this to me, I loved you baby girl?

Shane Trim (14)
Cardinal Pole RC School

A LIMBO CHALLENGE

I am a good limbo dancer
I try my best
I try to impress the judges
I concentrate.

My mind feels like it's going to burst,
My heart is beating fast, like somebody is banging a drum.
My legs are shaking like somebody is shaking a musical instrument.
My back feels like it's going to break.

I am trying not to worry
I am praying that I won't go wrong
I am thinking people will clap for me
I wonder if I'm strong.

My aim is to be the best
My aim is to smile
My aim is to clap for everyone else and
My aim is to beat the best limbo dancer - whose name is Kelsey
So stand back girl, because I'm gonna win!

Chanel Stanio (12)
Cardinal Pole RC School

PROMISE TOLD

P romises, promises, which Mum told
R eminders, reminders, which I mumbled
'O ut! Out!' Mum said. 'Now! Now!' she was stressed
'M um, mum!' I shouted once more. 'No! No!' she grabbed her paws.
 I n the house, all sad and glum, out of the house as quiet as a mouse.
'S appy and Zappy we're going to the shops,' said my little sister
     Vicky
E asily brought! As if I taught

T ime wasting, I am still waiting.
O h no! Oh no! She's brought my favourite toy
L et it go, it doesn't matter because she knows.
D id I say yes, or did I say no, she's brought my favourite toy?
                    You know!

Deborah Godji (12)
Cardinal Pole RC School

FLEXIBLE

I am twelve
I can tie myself into a knot
I am a gymnast.

I have ten gymnastic trophies
My mum keeps them in a safe place
My hobby is being flexible
My mum says, 'Mind you don't hurt yourself when you tie
yourself into a knot.'
My friends are sometimes jealous
When I get picked for a job by the teacher.

Deandra Harris (12)
Cardinal Pole RC School

ACROSTIC POEM

B reakfast time
R ectitude of work in the kitchen,
E ating their breakfast with enjoyment
A nd watching television.
K itchen used for cooking,
F ather was working
A nd children eating their breakfast whilst
S ensibly watching television.
T ime for breakfast.

T ime for their Dad to come in from work
I n that time, their Dad was in an accident
M other and children in stock
E vening passed - The Breakfast Time.

Jincy Eapen (12)
Cardinal Pole RC School

GET DOWN ON IT

'G et down on it!' shouted the crowd. 'Get down on it!'
　　　　　　I was petrified.
E dging to the left and edging to the right, I came down
　　　　　　with a fright.
T urned to the left, turned to the right,
　　　　　　under, under, with annoying lift.

D own, down I still go!
O h no, please don't let me touch the wall
W ay down touching the ground,
N early there, don't make a sound.

Belinda Bryden (12)
Cardinal Pole RC School

UNTITLED

T he ball goes in the net,
H elping Kewell herd the ball into the net
E ven better when Ryan Giggs runs

B all goes round and round, in the net
A ll over the place
L oved the crowd
L oved the goal of Kewell.

G o in the net
O ver the goalkeeper's hand,
E ven better when Scholes hit the crossbar.
S ad was the goalkeeper.

I n the net goes the ball
N ow they're winning!

N ever stood a chance
E ven better when Kewell hits the crossbar.
T he end of the match was bad, they had lost.

Byron Velastegui (12)
Cardinal Pole RC School

RAVE

Rave, rave, we love going to a rave
With the music all around the cave
We dance, dance all night long
Whilst the girls are waving and the beat is strong

There is base drumming into my head
Whilst youngsters are at home, safely tucked up in their beds
We queue up at the beginning of the night
But later on we witness a fight.

The excitement is electric
It's charging up the air
The boys hold up their lighters
The girls fix their hair

The music overtakes us
It pounds on through the night
The music of the rave is just fantastic
Right?

Charles Willoughby (14)
Cardinal Pole RC School

KEWELL SCORES A GOAL

K ewell scores all kinds of goals,
E arly goals he scores for Leeds.
W illing to score a goal, he hits the ball hard,
E ven in the match, he goes in hard with a tackle
L earning hard how to score
L inking up with the other players.

S coring goals like thunder
C reating set-ups for the goals,
O bviously he can score goals.
R ound and round the pitch he runs
E arning money, every day,
S uccess at last. I've finally scored.

A n unbelievable goal, he scores again and again.

G oals, glorious goals
O h no! He's missed. It was off target.
A fantastic game he has had
L aughing all day over his goals.

Matthew Crinnion (12)
Cardinal Pole RC School

THE ONE

One light, two lights, three, four, five lights
Hold it, green - g*o!*
The only time you'll get to see
22 cars at over 500bhp
Roaring down a narrow track
Races at the front and at the back.

Naturally a Ferrari's winning
What's that at the back? A Minardi, spinning
Into a Sauber - both in a barrier!
Debris everywhere, safety car - Ferrari despair.

Three laps it takes to clear the track
Safety car pulls in - now we're back
To the racing, full of speed and tension
Back markers with some apprehension.

Halfway through this 70-lap race
Williams trying to stick with the ferocious
Pace of the frighteningly fast Ferrari
Of Michael Schumacher.

Pit stop time. New tyres. More fuel
This is the period that could change it all
12 pit crewmen crowding round the car
Got new tyres, going well so far
Fuel pump out, you get the shout
You're ready to go and win.

Now it's time for the final lap
Williams have made up the ten second gap
It's a race to the finish, a race to the line.

Not long left - now's the time
The Williams goes for a daring move
But forgets and hits the groove
Of the kerb, it's too high.
The front of the car goes into the sky
And lands in the gravel trap.

The Ferrari wins a great race
But could you keep up with the intense pace
Of the one . . . Formula 1?

Steven Bush (14)
Cardinal Pole RC School

LUCKY GOAL

The lucky goal was when Harry Kewell
scored against Man Utd. Alan Smith got the ball
and made a little run down the wing, he crossed the ball,
Harry Kewell jumped about five feet in the air and headed it down.
Barthez nearly gets hit by Alan Smith's boot.
The ball slips through his legs and straight into the goal.
As they celebrate, Barthez gets a punch from David Beckham,
Barthez cannot open his left eye at all, when the full-time whistle goes,
Barthez gets up and throws Smith's boot on to Row K and when Smith
finds the man who has his boot, he punches the man and about 30,000
people come and beat him up. When they go into the tunnel,
Sir Alex Ferguson smashes a bottle over Barthez's head
and knocks him out cold.
Then all of Man Utd's team throw him out on to the pitch.
When Barthez wakes up he's in goal against Bayer Leverkuzen.
Man Utd are 1-0 up.
He keeps saying, 'Lucky goal! Lucky goal!'

Daniel O'Hagan (12)
Cardinal Pole RC School

FABIEN'S FAILURE

F ighting to try to save goals
A cting fast is the key to success,
B iting himself, making a mess,
I nternational superstar.
E veryone knows he loves his mum
N ever ever nervous
S ad singing.

F antastic Fabien
A lways ready,
I ncubus is how he acts.
L earning like a genius
U ndertaker
R eal man.
E dgar is the best.

Edgar Odompleh (12)
Cardinal Pole RC School

I AND MY

I am Lorraine and I am thirty
My children are hungry
I am making them breakfast
My husband isn't here
I've split up from him
My children and
I are happier alone
My children are going to school
I am taking them to school
My children love school.

Lorraine Douglas (12)
Cardinal Pole RC School

18

DANCING QUEEN

In the picture you can see
the girl dancing on her knees.
Bending her back under the pole,
moving towards the end.
She draws closer.

Everyone gathered together to see
what's going on.
She started to show off but everyone
didn't like her anymore.
But now she was just about to slip.

Everyone is sneaking and laughing
behind her back as she feels bad for
showing off.
She started to concentrate - and won!

Michelle Boyce (12)
Cardinal Pole RC School

DANCING QUEEN

I am the judge who decides who wins,
My friend sets up the limbo stick
I can see the girl struggling to pass the pole.
My friend has taken a picture
To put in the magazine.
I hear the music start to get louder as she starts.
My other friend, who is the judge as well,
Says her name is Sarah.
I watch carefully to see if she touches the pole,
My friend watches to see if she trips.
I think she is the winner.

Emma Brolly (12)
Cardinal Pole RC School

GUNNING

Sitting there, making no sound,
I would hear the roar of the crowd.

As we watched the entrance of our team,
I would hear the crowd shout and scream.

Arsenal Vs Chelsea, what a sight,
We all knew that this would be a fight.

The referee's whistle blows,
My excitement and fear shows.

Five minutes in, Chelsea takes the lead,
We worried how many we may concede.

Suddenly a penalty, crowd holds their breath,
Our exceptional player puts it in with his left.

Ten minutes later Ljungberg makes a run,
He's as fast as a bullet out of a gun.

Out of nowhere, another goal,
From the head of Ashley Cole.

The half-time whistle blew,
We're winning 2-1, phew!

But it's not over yet,
They'll equalise I bet.

The whistle blows again,
Oh no, it's started to rain.

Lampard crosses in the ball,
But Vieira clears no trouble at all.

Oh no, Hasselbaink volleys, making it 2-2,
The Arsenal crowd roar, 'Booo!'

Nearing the end,
Chelsea need to defend.

Henry shoots, scores!
The crowd roars.

The final whistle blows,
My jubilation and joyfulness shows.

I laugh and sing,
Great, another win!

Daniel Jones (14)
Cardinal Pole RC School

MY MUM

If my mum was a sweet
She'd be a jelly sweet
She would be very tasty.

If my mum was an insect
She'd be a butterfly
She would be the queen of the butterflies.

If my mum was a flower
She'd be a pink rose
Like a shiny rose in a tree.

If my mum was a chocolate
She'd be a Wispa
Tasty and crispy.

If my mum was a toy
She'd be Xena
Xena, the warrior princess.

Lanre Malaolu (12)
Cardinal Pole RC School

LEG-BREAKING LIMBO

L eg-breaking limbo, out on the beach
E very one cheering, 'Go girl! Do it for me
G ood one girl.'

B end a little bit more
R ather than panicking, think who you're doing it for.
E veryone knows what she is like
A nything for money, even a fight.
K ind is she?
I don't think so!
N evertheless
G o, go, go!

L ove doesn't matter to her,
I don't think so!
M emories come back
B efore you get to know
O h, she isn't a true friend after all!

Lauren Smye (12)
Cardinal Pole RC School

DADDY'S GIRL

I know, I know you're Daddy's little girl,
I know if you have a secret
You have to tell
Because you're Daddy's little girl
I know you love being Daddy's little girl
Because he treats you well!
Why are you Daddy's little girl?
Because he treats me badly but he treats you well.
I hate you being Daddy's little girl.

Hanif Best (14)
Cardinal Pole RC School

BREAKFAST

B   reakfast in the kitchen
R   eally nice chicken
E   very morning
A   ll of them are laughing
K   itchen is messy
F   ast eating kids
A   lmost finished
S   omeone is sleeping
T   ad is snoring in there

I   n time, kids finished eating
N   ow they are just leaving

K   icking the ball around
I   n the playground
T   hey enjoy it
C   alling their friends to join in
H   appy is everyone
E   xcept the dad
N   ow he's alone . . .

Greta Citronaite (12)
Cardinal Pole RC School

UNTITLED

She bent backwards
Backwards and backwards
Until I thought she would break
But she went under the pole
And the task was complete
Everyone cheered
And she smiled with glee.

Callum Walker-Hudson (12)
Cardinal Pole RC School

FOR BEING A SO-CALLED TEENAGER . . .

I hate being blamed for everything
For being a so-called teenager . . .
I hate getting shouted at
For being a so-called teenager . . .
I hate getting into trouble with my parents
For being a so-called teenager . . .
I hate arguing with the teachers at school
For being a so-called teenager . . .
I hate being accused of things I don't do
For being a so-called teenager . . .
I hate people giving me dirty looks
For being a so-called teenager . . .
I hate getting grounded by my parents
For being a so-called teenager . . .
I hate being punished by other people
For being a so-called teenager . . .
I wonder sometimes why I get treated like this?
That's why I hate being a so-called teenager . . .

Isaac Acheampong (14)
Cardinal Pole RC School

SOULMATE

A dark and thunderous place for me
Lit by the presence of the gun
Come closer . . . come closer
And surrender to
The dark side of the sun

A constant torrential rain in me
Continues beating, on and on
Come closer . . . come closer
And behold
The dark side of the sun

A swooshing hurricane within me
Grinding round, on and on
Come closer, come closer
And enter
The dark side of the sun.

Zipporah Okoye (12)
Cardinal Pole RC School

I HATE POETRY

I hate poetry
I didn't want to write this poem,
My teacher made me do it!
You see she doesn't understand about the St Lucian man
He hasn't those wicked rhyming words
And those crazy similes.
It just drives me mad, I'm a St Lucian man.

I hate poetry
It doesn't really have a meaning to me,
It's annoying, like an itch.
It doesn't have any liveliness to me, it's really a bitch.
It's sad, like a wet lovely dog,
It needs to be washed out, blow-dried and restyled.

I hate poetry,
Poetry is like Bethnal Green - dry, every day,
It's like seeing the same movie over and over again,
I don't like its ways.
Poetry is like when your mum just sits there watching
Cheers! Maurie Povich and Jerry Springer -
It's boring! I hate poetry.

Curtis Prospere (14)
Cardinal Pole RC School

Ball Curls Past Fabien

B all on fire,
A ctive Kewell scores the goal.
L eeds are happy
L eeds are happy!

C urly-haired Barthez has none,
U gly Barthez.
R unning out of the goal and letting people score.
L oser! Loser! Barthez you are a loser!
S tart Barthez crying, because of the goal.

P ower nodding from Kewell
A round the pitch, Kewell scored the goal.
S tarts Barthez sweating,
T umbling Barthez.

F ootball rolled into the goal,
A round the football pitch, Barthez tumbled.
B all going into the goal.
I ce on the pitch when Manchester United and Leeds were playing.
E nergetic Smith was sad on the football pitch.
N ow the match is over.

Harry Ayelabola (12)
Cardinal Pole RC School

Pupil Work

Pupil work from my point of view,
Is going to school
And sometimes playing the fool

Some teachers are funny
Some teachers are keen
Others are silly
But the rest are all mean

Homework we get, every single day
If you don't do it - er . . . I'd rather not say
In English we do poetry, plays and story writing
But in science we do tests, it's nail-biting

In school, girls and boys go out with each other
Ahh, isn't it cute, I call them young lovers.
When school ends, children scream and shout
This is the end of my poem piece - I'm out!

Natalie Ofori Nuamah (13)
Cardinal Pole RC School

I, MY CHILDREN AND HIM

I   n the house I stand all alone, very lonely, I hide it boldly.

M   y children do not know what is going on as they wonder if I'm down
Y   ours is mine and mine is yours.

C   hris, my son, listen always before you are gone.
H   arry, husband, happy and holy is all I needed.
I   n the midst of the morning - is *Him,* the one?
L   ife is not something that you can play with
D   on't disrespect your elders, I say again and again.
R   un like the wind whilst you feel the ray.
E   ventually you will find a way
N   ever forget what has happened.

A   ctive is what you are, never lose it when you're afar
N   ovice is what you are, never reject yourself
D   emand a good life, control your future.

H   e
I   s
M   e.

Charles Nnaji (12)
Cardinal Pole RC School

MY REPLY

I have listened to what you have to say
I understand where you are coming from,
What you have said though has had no impact on my decision.
All you have told me is your feelings for me are all lust.
I am a very religious girl
I do not believe in sex before marriage.
I will not have sex until I find the man I love,
I appreciate the flattery you have given to me
But I feel you just see me as prey.
If you continue to try and pressure me into sex
You might find yourself alone.
I would rather let the worms have my virginity,
Than to let someone have it whom I was not in love with.

Kieran McNamara (15)
Cardinal Pole RC School

NEW BABY

As I embrace her
Pressing her soft silky cheek close to mine
I can smell fresh rosy scent in her fine golden hair
Her eyes two sapphires glistening
Her smile makes it great to be there
For she is more beautiful than all the stars that shine at night
Her little body in my arms just fills me with delight
I know I will love her always,
Till death do us part
I know I will always have a special place for her
Deep down in my heart.

Amy Bracey (12)
Cardinal Pole RC School

A FOUR LETTER WORD

Love. A four letter word.
I once loved love, but yet I'm afraid of it.
I once cherished love, but then I vanquished it.
I've been scarred by the memories that were once there.
I've tried to run, I've tried to hide, but it seems to keep coming back.
The feelings that I had don't seem to go away.
This feeling called love is a mysterious thing.
It's never here to stay.
People fall in love everyday.
I once thought I was in love.
But think about it, what is love?
Feeling funny whenever they're near.
Fire laser burn, adrenaline rush occurs.
Love is a thing you can't put into words.
To me it's just a feeling.

Monique Cunningham (13)
Cardinal Pole RC School

I AM THE LIMBO DANCER

I am the limbo dancer
Going underneath the pole
Down and down I go
Sweating, my heartbeat is racing
I don't know what I'm going to be facing
Will they cheer or will they boo?
I don't know what they think about me
But when I win this competition I'll be happy
And grin with glee
As the announcer says the winner is
Me! Me! Me!

Latoya Commodore (13)
Cardinal Pole RC School

ONE NIGHT STAND

It took only one night
For me to realise that it wasn't right
At first I thought that it was okay
But in the end I ran away
I visited the doctor's clinic
He told me that I was stuck in it.

How would I be able to manage?
Everything that was earned is now damaged
I should have used protection
The love has died and so has the affection
I did it for a bit of fun
It was very childish and very dumb.

I'll face rejection from my family
They'll be upset and probably angry
Am I the only one who has made this mistake?
It was like a choice of lamb or fillet steak
Why am I always the bad penny?
I try to reassure myself that it happens to many.

By accident I have created a new life
In eight months time it will be a different strife
Where do I go from here?
My life has no meaning, it is really bare
What possessed me, why do I think this way?
It is called a romantic 'one night stand' I was led astray.

Rochelle Roberts (15)
Cardinal Pole RC School

CHOICE IN LIFE?

I am another fed up youth
Who's resorted to crime
Too dumb for university
School's just a waste of time

When I bop through my manor
My jeans are worn down low
It's important to have the right image
Wear Versace or Moschino

Of course I need a fast car
So I can get around
I'll probably have to hot-wire one
A cool car, that I've found

The excitement's great
When you're gonna snatch a bag
The excitement is profound
You know you're going to have success
Knock your victim to the ground

Yes robbery is the life for me
You see it's the way things have to be
Being branded a no hoper
At the age of sweet fourteen
Is my driving force
To do my worst
My cool image must be seen.

Marcus Philip (12)
Cardinal Pole RC School

EXPELLED ON MY FIRST DAY

I got to the playground, no one was there,
I couldn't help but stand and stare.
I stepped towards the building very cautiously
I don't know why, I was scared,
What was wrong with me?

I got to the entrance, a man stood
Next to the door
He looked kind of scruffy,
Damn, I thought I was poor!

He began tapping his watch signalling
That I was late.
I caught a glimpse of his watch
I knew it was a fake.

He opened the door, we both went in,
He began to walk, I started to follow.
I couldn't help staring at his nose it
Was so fat, ugly and hollow.

He stopped and opened a door,
In there stood a man
Beside him was a woman, she looked so old
And identical, she could have been his nan.

I sat down and heard him mutter
A word to the woman, something like *expel*
I sat there, my mouth hanging wide open
And I thought, what the hell!

Alcides Andre (14)
Cardinal Pole RC School

To Her Lusty Master

What is the rush?
We do have time,
Not all in the world
And I'm only twenty-nine
This little time we have
We should savour
And not waste on
Lewd behaviour
'Time's winged chariot'
Is not nearly here!
So you do have time
To stop and leer
Would it do you such harm
If all your lust
Was turned into dust?
After all, lust is
A deadly sin
And at this moment in time
I cannot see myself giving in.
I hope you're not taking this the wrong way
Because I do love you, I'm glad to say
And I also, sometimes full of sweet sensations,
Feel like giving into these temptations
But, I still don't feel ready, as such
So, if you lust for me this much
I believe that you can wait
Until this unspecified date.

Jason O'Hare (16)
Cardinal Pole RC School

THE JOYS OF SALSA

In his arms,
Tight and snug,
He controls my movements
To the song.

Trumpets booming,
Maracas shake -
The beat's vibrating
Through my veins.

Hand in hand
We can't stop moving -
It's time to spin,
I smile, approving.

All around are swirls of colours,
Of vibrant Spanish outfits
On beautiful Spanish girls.
I know I look different
With skin so brown,
But I can't stop clenching
To my gorgeous Spanish man.

I gaze into his green eyes
As he signals the next move.
Now my grip loosens
But we stay joined at the tips.
With a graceful twirl
I land into his care -
And groups of people start to stare

Because . . .

In his arms,
Tight and snug,
He controls my movements
To the song.

Doreen Ojegba (14)
Cardinal Pole RC School

HOW DO I LOVE YOU?

How do I love you?
You can't count the ways
What I feel for you is strong
I know it's not a phase.

I love you so much,
Sometimes I can't breathe
When I see you smile
My heartbeat begins to cease.

I feel your presence
When you're not even there
The warmth of your body,
Your hand on me, here.

You're a part of my heart
You're a part of my soul
You're the part that was missing
But now I am whole.

How do I love you?
You can't count the ways
There's too much in my heart
And not enough days.

Natalie Obeng-Mensah (17)
Cardinal Pole RC School

MY FAVOURITE WEST INDIAN SHOP

The typical West Indian shop
Is very boring and doomed for a drop.
But my favourite West Indian shop
Is heading to zoom straight to the top.

Forget Mummy's cooking,
Forget Granny G's,
All I want is my bun and cheese,
My curry goat and my rice and peas.

My favourite West Indian shop
Is pure West Indian, non-stop.
No pie and mash, bangers or trout,
So they tell the Englishman to 'hush him mout'.

For a snack it's all about the patties
Or dumpling, saltfish and ackee.
Main course could be the roti,
But then you get cussed by Grandpapi.

Sometimes for Sunday din-dins
We go to my favourite West Indian shop.
We'll have oxtail and butter beans,
Fish, chicken or red pea soup.
Whatever it is,
I'll finish it in a swoop.

The typical Englishman orders jerk chicken,
While others stand choosing and picking.
He'll watch and eat finger-licking, saying,
'Oh jolly! What marvellous chicken!'
While the ladies nearby get into a heat,
And ask, 'Why de ass he watch me fe eat?'

The air is filled with the sound of reggae,
While everyone drinks BIGGA or KA.
People buy their porridge and fish,
Life never stops
In my favourite West Indian shop.

Rochelle Greenidge (14)
Cardinal Pole RC School

DREAMS

Lucy heard some terrible news
She just could not go on.
She felt that she had lost her heart and soul,
Her dreams, her love.

She is 25, she has a child
How is she going to cope?
She had a husband.
He's gone! He's gone!
Why! Tell me why?
He's gone! He's gone!
Why! Tell me why?

She has a job to do
She just can't sit and cry
She has to do it
She succeeds.

She wins
She's not happy at all
Her love has gone
Her soul, her dreams
Her love.

Kelsey Davis (12)
Cardinal Pole RC School

My Life

I'm not an animal or a
Thing either.
An imbecile? An invalid?
No, neither.
I'm a human being like
Everyone else.
I have skin and blood
And a normal pulse.
Just walk past me, leave
Me alone.
Leave me to rot and die
On my own.
None have feelings for me,
Unless you count hatred.
I'm seen as something
Disgusting and putrid.
I maybe on junk, smack,
Coke and weed,
But don't chastise me or
Condemn me to lead
A good life after all I've
done.
That's why I'm on the run.

Leianne Walrond (14)
Cardinal Pole RC School

MY FAMILY

My name is Richard
And here's my family.

My mum is moany and really groany
Always giving chores out
If someone farts she will look at you with disgust

My dad is bald, but cool
And loves football.
He's always over at Highbury
Cheering and singing,
'Arsenal have won the double!'

My brother Danny is like a granny
He never stops talking,
And he really hates walking.

My brother Terry is an angel
In school that is.
At home he moans
At us for breathing too loudly.

That is my family,
You may think they're strange
But to me
They're just a strain!

Richard Sacker (14)
Cardinal Pole RC School

LOVE

Love is really painful,
A second-hand emotion
A sort of tradition, affection, infatuation
Love helps you grow,
Helps you know what to prepare when someone important loves you so.
Love is appreciated, not hated
If it was like that there
Would be no rope of hope
For the evil world, just a downhill slope.
Apparently, it's based on positivity
Presented as violet, rose, a lily or even a daisy.
True love is all of these things
Not just gold wedding rings.
Love is like a warm summer breeze,
When cold and loveless,
It caresses and blesses.

Joshua Okungbaiye (14)
Cardinal Pole RC School

DO YOU?

I don't know why the sky is blue
Or why the raindrops scattered through
Or why the grass is wet with dew.

Do you?

I don't know why the sun is round
Or why a seed grows in the ground
Or why the thunder makes loud sounds

Do you?

I don't know why the clouds are white
Or why the moon shines so bright
Or why the air turns black at night

Do you?

Princeston Cole (14)
Cardinal Pole RC School

BULLY BOY

His thuggish behaviour is nasty
His thuggish behaviour is cruel
His thuggish behaviour is savage and sly
Just like him to torment me
And then act cool.

When I feel him present
I know I'm in for affliction
I sense an indescribable repugnance
He won't stop - it's like his addiction

My heart begins to vibrate
As I know he lies in wait
He's cunning as a fox on the run
He hides his cruelty
When adults come

And yet he is like a captor, trapping me
I'm his hostage, longing to break free
What do I do to make him so angry?
When will he leave me in peace and let me be me?

What can I do to beat the bully?

Shola Christian (12)
Cardinal Pole RC School

REASONS TO WAIT
(Reply to Andrew Marvell's 'To His Coy Mistress')

Patience is a virtue my darling
And I certainly won't deny,
That my love for you is as deep as an ocean
But firstly we both must try . . .

To communicate mentally with emotions,
To ensure that our love won't die.
Before we take that great large step
And I find that our love is a lie.

You have to see my point of view
Our relationship is not a race
Of how quickly you can get me into bed
Please, for me, slow down your pace!

Where do you think the time's going?
Why are you in such a rush?
Take time to touch the depths of my soul
And turn my bones into slush.

It is then that I will be ready
To give myself fully to you,
To allow you to devour my body
And confirm our relationship is true.

To me you are my entire world,
You are the blood rushing through my veins.
To me you are the reason to live,
You are the slayer of my pains.

But yet am I to be completely convinced
That I mean the same to you.
So calm your lust and earn my trust
That after consummation I won't be blue.

Domini Connor (16)
Cardinal Pole RC School

SITTING ON THE STAIR

I'm hiding here, sitting under the stair
I hope to god he doesn't hear me sitting silent as he draws near.

It's my dad, he's so big, six foot five to be exact.
My mum, she's so small, so fragile, so intact
She's not very tall, not rich, not grand.
She can't be perfect, but she should really try and take a stand.
When his hand flies towards my face
Why does she just look into open space?
And when he's done she sees to my distress
Comforts me, cleans up my messes
And then she'll say how sorry she is
How she doesn't know how it came to this.

I remember before it was like this
He'd only ever touch me with a loving kiss
But that was before he took to drink
And I suppose he forgot to think
It used to be different, he used to hit Mum
And that, believe me, wasn't much fun.
One night I stood up to him, like a fool
He slapped me down, which wasn't cool.
From then on I was his new target
Oh how I hate that stupid man.
I have his bruises all over my back
Self-confidence is what I lack.
No one knows, it's a secret you see
These lines are just between you and me.

I'm hiding here, sitting under the stair
I hope to god he doesn't hear me sitting,
Oh my god he's here.

Cartiere Campbell (14)
Cardinal Pole RC School

SEASONS

Spring comes when days are longer and it gets slightly warmer,
Spring comes when flowers begin to bloom and leaves begin to
reappear,
Spring comes when true love gets a breath of fresh air
And spring comes when you start a new school year.

Summer comes when the sun decides to show its face,
Summer comes when the sky is blue and clear.
Summer comes when the ice cream van plays that melody.
Summer comes when nights get shorter and days get longer.

Autumn comes when leaves start to disappear,
Autumn comes when nights are slightly longer and days are a bit
shorter.
Autumn comes when days are dry and the weather is cold and the
moon is high.

Winter comes when it doesn't stop raining,
Winter comes when we are all complaining that we are wet and cold,
we all get the flu.
We have to stay inside, with nothing to do,
Then Christmas comes and brings us cheer,
There's food, there are presents and we all have a happy new year.

Jvein Edwards (14)
Cardinal Pole RC School

CHOCOLATE

You might not think it, but people are very similar to chocolate,
We can be really sweet or really bitter,
We can be soft or hard, it depends where we are.
We come in all shapes and sizes,
We all look different and have different appearances,

We are all different colours,
We are all made differently and moulded into different things.
We are deep, classy, smooth, addictive, adorable,
Irresistible, tempting, luscious, delicate, stylish and tasty.
Just like chocolate!

Gary Cumber (15)
Cardinal Pole RC School

WHAT DID I DO?

When a crime is committed, everyone blames me,
Just because I'm a black boy wearing a hoodie,
I like to wear caps and wear my jeans low
And my friends and I, all live around Bow.

When we're walking on the street or getting a bus,
The police will appear and straight away stop us,
'We didn't do anything. We're just on our way home,'
'You all fit the description of the thief of a mobile phone!'

When we try to speak they just say, 'Shut it!
Do as we say, now all empty your pockets.'
They were two white men, one short, one fat,
They were both wearing uniforms, but neither wore a hat.

They tell us to wait while they call HQ
So we did what they said, we didn't know what else to do,
The criminals were caught earlier that day,
So the police got in their car and just drove away.

The criminals turned out to be two white men,
But I know this will all probably happen again.

Sean Joseph (15)
Cardinal Pole RC School

TEENAGE DIRTBAG

Teenagers, teenagers
they never work for dads.
Teenagers, teenagers
they are never, never glad.
Teenagers, teenagers
they are dirty and smell bad.
Teenagers never do this, never do that,
they never do washing up for their mum,
they leave their plates till the scum just runs,
that's what teenagers do.

Most teenagers are punks
that listen to rock,
they skateboard all the time
and bop to hip hop,
they dress with ripped jeans
and baggy hoods over their heads.

That's what teenagers are
and that's what they do.

Andrew Philippedis (15)
Cardinal Pole RC School

EXAM RESULTS

Mum, Mum, Mum,
My results have just come through
Should I open it?
Should I leave it?
You open it
Wait, wait, wait,
What will I do if it's bad?
Will I take it again
Or will I just struggle through my life?

Maybe I should leave it
But it might be good news
I might get 5 A's
And be the best doctor in the world
You know what Mum
You open it and tell me
Oh my god!
I've passed
I always knew I would.

Crispian Ndu-Seaba (15)
Cardinal Pole RC School

TALKING IS ALL SHE EVER DID

Talking is all she ever did
Feeling the vibrating
Of her upper lip
Her tongue rasping
To the words she releases
The slush, harsh, cold words
She always uses

Now her tongue is
Diving down and up
Stalking her teeth one by one
Loving the attention her tongue is receiving
While everybody else is laughing

Slowing down now
The vibrating's stopped now
The rasping's over
Finished
Talking is all she ever did.

Jackie Field (14)
Cardinal Pole RC School

ALLEYWAY

Walking down the street
Shopping bag in hand
Suddenly I realise,
I'm being followed by a man.
I jerk my head around
He's not a foot away
His dirty hand curves over my mouth
There's nothing I can say.
Hauled into the alleyway
Rusty garbage cans
Contrast with the gleaming knife
That's brandished in his hand!

I scream
And scream
And scream
I struggle and I wait
I realise there goes my life
And surrender to my fate.

Neva Frederick (12)
Cardinal Pole RC School

TRUE LOVE

Not a rose or a satin heart
Could it be real,
Or could it be my imagination?
But everyday I do see you in my room,
Late at night when all is asleep.
You sneak into my bedroom
And you sit by my bed,
You show me a love that is so real
Take me into a world I wish could be mine.

A burning flame of something
More than infatuation,
A true love that for me
Has an uncertain future.
Or maybe in another world, my love,
In another world
You may know me
But I not you.

Aghogho Gharoro-Akpojotor (16)
Cardinal Pole RC School

TO HER IMPATIENT MASTER

We've got all the time in the world.
Wait until it's my time,
Because I'm not ready to submit to your lies.
I don't believe my beauty dies,
Nor flies away in time's cruel power.
You wait, until it is my hour.
It will be kept for you but,
We need to wait,
Let's take things slowly, it is our fate,
I know the time is coming for us.
You flatter me so very much.
It's much appreciated, my dear,
But I won't preserve my virginity for years,
But let the time come, when it's right for me.
You shouldn't rush me into it, can't you see?
For the time will come,
When this situation will be forgotten.
My body is yours, it won't go rotten.
Can you see I want to save my love for you,
Will last beyond the grave.

Joseph Daini (15)
Cardinal Pole RC School

BLACK, BEAUTIFUL AND PROUD

Recognise this, recognise me
I isn't Portuguese, Asian or Chinese,
I'm a girl of her roots, born and bred
Ackee, saltfish and dumpling is what I'm fed.

Recognise this, see my brown face
'Coz I will always win you in a race,
Genuine and intelligent, I will succeed
'Coz nothin' in this world comes for free.

Young and talented I may be
But I is a black girl *very* classy and sexy,
Look at me, stare
You will realise there ain't nothin' I fear.

Racist comments won't hold me down
Nothin' you do or say will make me frown,
All I am sayin' is don't cross me when I'm vex
'Coz you don't want to see this black girl flex.

Don't take no crap from no one
Take everything in your stride,
One thing that I value the most
Is, but of course, my pride.

Black history
It's like a mystery,
Hidden and unknown
It's like it's hidden in a cushion and then deeply sown.

Help the youths of the world today
So that we can stand together and pray,
Stand together as a unity
Unite, like a community.

Go to school and do your best
For, only there you will be guaranteed success.

Louise James (15)
Cardinal Pole RC School

MY MUM AND I

Smiling all the time whether I've been good or bad,
She's the best role model I've ever had.

The years we had so far are good,
The way I know it always should.

The love I have for her is strong
And her's the same, even if I'm wrong.

She supports me in the things I do,
Even if every day my ideas are new.

Regardless if things go bad,
She seldom ever gets mad.

To resolve problems we have girl talks
And if necessary we go for walks.

My mother, my best friend,
Always there right to the end.

Smiling all the time whether I've been good or bad
She's the best role model I've ever had.

Melissa Bethune (14)
Cardinal Pole RC School

BOFFIN

What are you doing, boffin?
Aren't straight As enough for you?
I bet when you grow up
You might teach teachers
And give them detentions,
Like I get when I am bad.

What are you doing, boffin?
Trying to solve your formulas
Theorems and Algebra problems?
You fly through exams,
As if you're flying in air
But I have to wade through it
As if I am in a thick pool of mud.

What are you doing, boffin?
Trying to impress the girls?
And that could have happened,
If you were like me
And not such a boffin
You can do their homework
And think you are a cool cat
But you will never be anyone like me.

What are you doing, boffin?
Trying to become a scientist
Mixing stuff up that can kill you?
But that's good
You can teach me to make stink bombs.

What's the deal with you, boffin?
You live in a nightmare
Why do you show that you are good

For all the world to see?
I don't understand you, boffin
You think you do the right stuff
But it could be wrong.

Be my friend, boffin
And then you can be good at anything and also be cool.

Lijo R Prasad (15)
Cardinal Pole RC School

MY BEST FRIEND

There are no secrets when we are together
Keeping us apart people could never
Although I know we quarrel and fight
We end up talking and our voices take flight
It's amazing how sometimes we hear no one else speak
In our own little world where it's never bleak.

There are no secrets when we are together
We come as a pair we never tether
I sometimes think I know people well
But they prove me wrong
They're two-faced liars all along
But never her, she's always there, through the
Fears and tears for all these years.

There are no secrets when we are together
We are always sure to speak to each other
When our pride has been dented
Isn't that why friends were invented?
I'm there for you
You're there for me
That's the way it will stay and should always be!

Emma Moore (14)
Cardinal Pole RC School

BLIND LOVE

I love you
And you love me
So why is everyone
Blind to see!

They say you don't love me
They say you don't care
But they're just jealous
Of the bond we share

No matter what they say
No matter what they do
I am going to show them
That our love is true.

Naomi Adams (14)
Cardinal Pole RC School

BEING A TEENAGER

Being a teen
I am so keen
I can finally play for my dream football team
I will be number 15
Being a teen
You have to have top gear
I will wear an earring in my ear
Being a teen
I want to be one forever
So I can stay young forever
So I don't have to pay taxes ever
Being a teen is what I want to be.

Ryan Healy (14)
Cardinal Pole RC School

WRONG JUDGEMENT

A black man driving a big car
Policemen watch him from afar
They check his registration
They take him to the station
A black man not driving his big car.

They check out his licence
No tension but just endurance
They check out his legal status
No anger, not the faintest.

A model citizen, surely not!
Must be selling crack or pot.
Can he be a role model for his nation?
We can find out through interrogation.

'Sorry Your Honour,'
Listen to the apologies
We say, 'We had no idea you were a . . . judge!'

Menalik Richards (13)
Cardinal Pole RC School

ABYSS

The sea is a gigantic puddle
Smooth and calm,
Rippling endlessly,
Sleeping like a baby until it wakes . . .
Screaming, crying, whooshing, crashing
For what seems like forever,
Crushing and drowning whatever is on it,
Eventually it stops, everything is calm, it is sleeping
Beautifully.

Sean Martin & Adam Reay (13)
Cardinal Pole RC School

UNDER THE NET

I'm on the edge
Waiting for the ball to be passed to me
The ball comes like a gush of wind
With a great spin
It came like a ball of fire
As I smell the burning rubber on the ball
It comes under a hot burger, it cools
I move into space
Another member of the team caught it
It looked crispy
Like a just-cooked sensation
Then it comes to me
Clack, it went into my hand
Red and steamy
I'm on the edge
I shoot; it leaves my hand from the tips of my fingers
It goes through, *swoosh!* a sound I like to hear
I was so happy
Excitement went through my veins at 70mph
As it got to my heart
It exploded, through my gullet to my mouth
I screamed, 'Yes!'
I ran sliding on the floor
Gliding like a leaf floating down a stream
I got my medal
The gold reflected from my eyes
I held it proudly, like I had won the lottery.

Sean Ayeltigah (14)
Cardinal Pole RC School

DINNER LADIES

Food, when home-made, is delicious and sweet,
How I hate those school lunches, at the knees make me weak.
Mouth-watering posters delude you it'll be a feast,
But the smells from the canteen could change an angel into a beast.

The dinner ladies are actually flesh-eating aliens under the skin,
Trying to hypnotise you through the logo on the spinach tin.
The spiral design attracts all who are frail,
The mentally impure the test will fail.

I hate the way teachers receive special lunches,
And attracting attention, continues, munches.
Upon golden plates they're served juicy steaks,
Whilst we students, in dog bowls, get rubber fakes.

I've seen those alien creatures, dinner ladies I mean!
Scratching their bums and then serving us as if clean.
Those disgusting dinner ladies in shaking their hair,
Release more candyfloss than you could get at a fair.

The majority of the time, food's too salty or sweet,
That's why we have food fights, leaving everything nice and neat.
Those horrible dinner ladies are then left cleaning till late,
Gathering all the remains for school lunches at a later date.

They recycle foods over and over, how sick can you get?
Probably adding bits and pieces of an alien pet.
That's why I switched to packed lunches, it's safer that way,
No more cheesecakes of cement, or pizzas of clay.

Eddy Attang (15)
Cardinal Pole RC School

MOTHERLY LOVE

I see my mum
As she moves
Through the crystal clear floor

She's holding a baby
Like her life is in her hands
She's looking at the baby
Like it's a sparkling diamond

She smiles at the baby with joy
Just knowing that she will be with it
For one more second makes her
Glow like the sunshine

Her smile bounces off the clean worktop
She wishes that the baby could be with her
Forever just so that she can become
Overwhelmed with joy

I only dream of one thing
To be in her arms
That are filled with love and joy.

John Diaz (14)
Cardinal Pole RC School

GOTH QUEEN

I stand and watch as you point and stare
You laugh at me and the clothes that I wear
You probably think when you look at me
You see a Marilyn Manson wannabe.
I have lots of body piercings and long dark hair
Is this why you choose to stand and glare?
No tan to see, my face is pale and white
Tell me, is this why you want to fight?

Look closer, look deep!
And see the person beneath

I'm the same as you and you
Emotions, feelings, flesh and blood too.
My goth image is my choice, my fashion identity,
It makes me different, it makes me *me!*

Cynthia Anipole (15)
Cardinal Pole RC School

FRIENDS ARE THERE

When you're having a bad time
When you've had a long cry
When someone has gone and died
When you've failed your English exam
Friends are there

When you're angry with someone else
When you haven't got any lunch money
When everyone else has gone
When you need a shoulder to lean on
Friends are there

When you need cheering up
When you're all alone
When you just want to moan
When you need a good laugh
Friends are there

When you need some help
When you're on your last hope
When you cannot cope
When you're fed up with your life
Friends are there.

Daniel Defreitas (15)
Cardinal Pole RC School

MY DRUM

When I play my drum
I always hear someone.
I try to play it to my best
Between every three quavers there's a rest.

My drum is shiny blue
A nice shiny blue from when I bought it new.
The seven pieces altogether
Will live in my room forever.

11 22 11 22 33
The rhythm gives melody to me
To me my drum is like a drug
Like nature's ladybird bug.

The snap of the hi-hat
The echo of the snare
Like the roar of a wild cat
That I could hardly bear.

When I play my drum
I always hear someone.

Emmanuel Oladimeji (15)
Cardinal Pole RC School

TEENAGE TERRORS

What do you think when you look at me?
A thug? A truant? But that's not what I want to be!
Okay . . . so I fight, though it's not right,
But I still do my best and pass my tests!
'Cause I wear hoodies and platinum too,
Doesn't mean I do the things you think I do!
I get into trouble and cause lots of strife,
But that's the down part in my life!

It's the influence I get from the people I know,
But that's how peer pressure goes.
I try to rise above and make my family proud,
But I keep getting dragged down by the wrong crowd!
Now it's time to let those people depart,
Put an end to all those broken hearts,
Put a smile to all those frowns,
And put an up to all those downs!

Anneke Nelson (15)
Cardinal Pole RC School

WHAT DO YOU SEE?

What do you think
     When you see me on the news?
An ordinary person or a stereotypical youth?
     One of the seven stereotypes?
A beautiful little angel
     Or a troublesome little tyke?
A completely innocent victim of a crime
     Or one of the 'kids these days'
On drugs all the time?
     A perfect kid who does really well at school
Or an accessory of my parents?
     A simple media tool?

In reality, I am none of these
     Nor am I one of the cute kids
Whose face never fails to please.
     I am a real person,
So when we pass each other in the street
     Look beyond the stereotype,
Look closer, see me.

James Smith (15)
Cardinal Pole RC School

THE OBSESSION

Finally *Saturday* is here
We're *Arsenal!* We should have nothing to fear

The team news comes in, in comes *Freddie*
It's been *two months*, is he ready?

Last year we *drew!*
Why? Because the *referee never had a clue*

The *whistle* blows!
My *anticipation, fear and excitement shows*

The *radio* crackles
Vieira slides in with one of his tackles

We're on the attack, *Wiltord down the wing*
The *Highbury crowd chant and sing!*

In comes Wiltord's *ball*
Toure jumps high and tall!

Smash! Into the net!
Wham! Goes Tony Gayel's bet

But who cares, we're *winning*
The Highbury crowd are *chanting and singing*

What a *joyous, happy* feeling
We're *leading!*

The other team is on the *attack*
All I can hear is deafening silence then a loud *crack!*

They had hit the *crossbar!*
Their player was out too *far!*

The half-time *whistle* goes
My *relief* shows

The whistle blows for the *second half*
Henry gets a challenge right on the *calf*

The commentators, the crowd and me are shouting, *'Send him off!'*
The referee gives him a yellow! *He let him off*

Henry takes the *free kick*
Wham, off the far *stick*

On the rebound, it's *Cole*
Yes! We've got that all-important second *goal*

The other team kick-off *again*
In the pulsating *rain!*

In comes a *high ball*
Vieira stands high and *tall*

He *heads it away*
The player chases Henry, *he won't catch him* anyway

A cross-field pass to *Ljungberg*
It's typical *Ljungberg surge!*

He shoots, *goooaaalll!*
He lobbed the keeper who's *tall and all!*

That should be *game, set and match*
At 3-0 we should be *impossible to catch*

The final whistle *blows*
My *relief, excitement and jubilation* shows

Yes! We're top of the league!
Are we really unstoppable?

Dipak Bhundia (14)
Cardinal Pole RC School

PORTRAIT

There she stood. Silent
Not exactly but almost
Everything silent except
The medium tempo music
Playin' softly in the background
Her paintbrush flowed in the beat with the music
Fast, small strokes
Slow, long strokes
Whatever the beat of the song
The beat her brush will play on paper
The beat would change
The brush stroke will change
Everything about her
Simple but flashy
Old but modern

Her hair always matched her mood
As well as her clothes and portraits
She looked dull but bright
At all times of the day
Just like her portraits
They matched those who looked upon it
Similarities which occur
Hypnotising portraits
Which trap you in a daze
Of shapes and colour
Your own world of privacy
Portraits which connect with you
As if you painted it yourself.

Zerlina Agyeman-Duah (14)
Cardinal Pole RC School

AS I WALK DOWN THE STREET!

As I walk down the street
I see the leaves blowing
The sun glowing
Children listening
And their faces glistening
As they listen to their
Parents talk.
As I walk down the street
I feel as if I haven't got
A care in the world.
I'm as free as a bird
Flying in the sky.
As I walk down the street
I see different kinds of faces
Of different races
And all sorts of ages.
As I walk down the street
I see a homeless woman
With a child
I think to myself what could
Be going on in their minds?
What could've happened to them?
What situation could they have
Been in?
As I walk down the street
I think to myself what is
Happening to the world?
I see the world deteriorating
Right in front of my eyes.
As I walk down the street.

Kaila-Tiye Baptiste (13)
Cardinal Pole RC School

HERE SHE IS

Crying
Sighing
It's all I can do
Forget the baby, she's only two

This twirling, swirling sick feeling, stuck inside me
Is incomprehensible
Mum says it's jealousy
How can I tell people?
How can I explain?
I'm feeling sad and left out, forgotten
My life is full of pain
I ask Mum again, hasn't she known
Since the baby has come
I feel all alone
No one to talk to
No one to befriend
I wish this lonely feeling would come to an end.

Pamela Ofoedu (12)
Cardinal Pole RC School

EXPECTATIONS
(Reply to Andrew Marvell's 'To His Coy Mistress')

You my dear sir, have the cheek,
To call me to bed after only one week,
You expect me to come running, on the word of command,
But you must be mistaken, I am not yet that fond.

I am sure of the fact, you have fallen for my looks,
But you have not yet learnt of women, among all those books.
A woman takes her time and likes to make a man wait,
You will never bed a woman by telling her it's fate.

A woman is intelligent, even more so than a man,
And for every situation, comes a ready-made plan.
For this type of problem, I am to give you a slap,
But that would do nothing to a womanising chap.

I look down on you in pity, of the fact you'll never marry,
Maybe impregnate a woman, with a baby to carry.
You men ignore whatever we mutter, but in the future will pay,
When women run this world in a more sensitive way.

Lucas Tsokallis (16)
Cardinal Pole RC School

REPLY TO HIS COY MISTRESS

(In reply 'To His Coy Mistress' by Andrew Marvell)

Oh, but we do have a world of time,
My coyness to you should not be a crime.
We have so much time to sit and talk,
Or go to the park and take long walks.
We should savour our love, we have plenty of time.

We can sit and talk forever my love
And gaze up at the stars above.
If you truly love me, you should understand,
You would not continue with your strong demands.
We should savour our love, we have plenty of time.

Why do you demand? Why do you threat?
There is still time yet.
We have all the time in the world in fact
Why do you feel the need to pressure me like that?
We should savour our love, in time it will grow,
For now we should just take it slow.

Dominique Hippolyte (15)
Cardinal Pole RC School

MY CAT

She walks in with her swift body
Taking no notice of anybody
Taking pride in the way she walks
Maybe even when she talks

She is so contented
When she's being fed
Cleaning herself every day
Possibly in every way

She looks at me with her big eyes
As wide as stars
That reach all the way to Mars
Whatever is instore is a big surprise

Now she sits and relaxes
Sprawled out on the carpet
Fur everywhere, like every pet
She drifts off to sleep
Falling into her world
When she awakes, she's back in my world.

Bianca Marquez (14)
Cardinal Pole RC School

FEELINGS

I'm not in the mood, I'm feeling drowsy,
I feel like drowning in the blue sea,
They restricted Beyblades, it's just insane,
It makes me feel so much pain,
I feel like punching my teacher, she gets on my nerves,
I feel like leaving the room, for better or worse.

Samson Odelowo (12)
Cardinal Pole RC School

TO MY LUSTY MASTER

(Mistress's reply 'To His Coy Mistress' by Andrew Marvell)

Your flattery is much appreciated,
But I must beg you to understand,
I do not want to hurry,
You'd appreciate this if you were a man,
But I'm beginning to have some doubts,
About this relationship we are in,
I do not think you are good for me,
Your mind is full of sin,
You know I'm deeply religious,
So this deed I cannot do,
I cannot seal our strong and true love,
Until I'm committed to you.
And if you find it hard to endorse
This belief I hold
I might just wait to give the worms,
My virginity, heart and soul.

Ryan Keogh (15)
Cardinal Pole RC School

CHANGING

My life is changing,
It's rearranging,
When I look in the mirror there's a stranger staring back at me.

The familiar face I see is no more,
Must've gone when I went out of the door,
What I remember has slipped from my brain,
Making me feel insane.

Aaron Bennett (13)
Cardinal Pole RC School

REPLY TO MY LUSTY MASTER

What's the rush?
We do have time
Let's just wait
And see what time would offer
Don't get me wrong
I do love you
But I don't feel I'm ready.

I love your smile
It makes me smile
You're always there when I need you
You're my lucky star
Which guides my way
And if you love me the way I do you
You'll wait maybe a day, a week, year or two
Until I feel ready
Our relationship must be more steady.

Mary Fadairo (15)
Cardinal Pole RC School

I HAVE TO LET YOU GO
(A reply to Andrew Marvell's 'His Coy Mistress')

Patience is a wonderful thing
It's something you must learn
Something you will never have
As long as for my love you yearn.

That 'long preserved virginity'
Is precious and most divine
Listen carefully and you will find
That this girl is leaving you behind.

If you cannot embrace
The finer things in life
I'll have no choice but to let you go
My answer to you is simply, no.

Roanne Jones (16)
Cardinal Pole RC School

SHADOW

This person is my shadow
Goes everywhere I go
Although I can never see him, he is always there
Watching me, loving me, surrounding in the air
Conversing with him is what I like to do
I never get an answer, but that doesn't matter at all
The love I have for him is stuck deep inside my heart
He is my heartbeat
Without that beat I cannot live
He's like a shining star
That glows and never goes away
I speak to him every single day

Words can't express exactly how I feel
Just that this person is very special to me
Why I feel this way? I'm not too sure
I love him day by day, more and more
This person knows my secrets
This person knows my thoughts
This person is like my blood that pulsates
In and around my body
Stimulates my mind, keeps me alive
This person is my saviour
This person is my shadow.

Gemma Samuels (14)
Cardinal Pole RC School

BEING A TEENAGER

Being a teenager
Causes so much stress,
It can make you happy
And also depressed.
Responsibility comes in teenagers' lives,
Changes occur in your body,
You start to realise,
You start to go through a particular phase,
Emotions are taken to a higher stage.
Someone from the other sex
Can break your heart.
Mix-ups occur,
Friends fall apart,
Mothers are scared
Of the outside world.
Fathers get scared
For their little girls.
Parents are scared
Because of all the dangers
But we have to live a bit
We're teenagers!

Precious Douaihy (14)
Cardinal Pole RC School

FRIENDS

I feel it's very wrong of me,
But I have to admit,
When someone offers friendship,
I have to have all of it,
I wouldn't want anybody else,
To have my friends with me,
I just want one, one special one,
Who's always there for me.

Thinks I'm better than all the rest,
Who never leaves my side,
Who doesn't listen to what others have to say,
Who lets me come and hide,
Within his heart, within his house,
It doesn't matter where, it doesn't matter when,
Who lets me be myself,
Through thick and thin.

Samantha Brown (12)
Cardinal Pole RC School

LIFE GOES ON

A moment in time
you'll never forget
the lack of time spent
you'll always regret.
The day someone so close to me died
all I did was sat and cried
can't help but to stay
remembering the past.
You stand still
but life . . . moves so fast.
Don't want to forget them
now that they're gone
but I know I've got to
because life goes on.
As hard as it seems I'll find my way
I'll look forward to a brighter day
but why did they leave,
where have they gone?
No questions answered
yet life goes on.

Sharon Purdy (15)
Cardinal Pole RC School

REMEMBER!

Remember when I was really small
And things seemed less important then?
Extravagances of Christmas past.
The love and warmth of every friend.
But time, it moves so quickly on
Unlike the hands, that seem to crawl.

Remember my youth, so careless and free.
Each day a joy to live my life.
But those days quickly ebb and fade
Just like the tide in seaward surf.
Each day the pattern reproduced,
New changes to my life and me.

Remember my teens, such carefree times,
Apart from my scholarship chores
Each day more different than before,
Like the opening and closing of many doors.
But the years they now so swiftly pass,
Like the memories of those distant rhymes.

So now look forward to a 'grown-up' world,
Where tasks and targets are 'all the rage'.
Each day monotonous, drags and grinds
Like the ageing actor on the same old stage.
Those years far gone, I wish for now,
Remembrances, like a flag unfurled.

Louise Leahy (16)
Cardinal Pole RC School

CHAMPIONS!

Every Saturday I would wait for the chant
To hear the Highbury crowd rage and rant.

Sitting there with my cup of tea
That was all needed for me.
Nervously I would await
As Grandad decided our fate.

The opposition fans would shout and jeer
Like they had nothing to fear.
When they see the Arsenal, they stop in their tracks
They know they have to watch their backs.

Half-time arrives, time for our snack,
Hoping the opposition can't claw back.

The second half starts with a blow of the whistle,
Come on Arsenal!
We're playing Partick Thistle.

Overall we're the better team,
'We're the best,' Grandad would beam.
The final whistle blows, a job well done,
Another fine day in the October sun.

Every Saturday I would wait for the chant,
To hear the Highbury crowd rage and rant.

Daniel Maguire (15)
Cardinal Pole RC School

REGRETS

So now that you are dead my dear, so now that you are dead,
I must walk the path of grief alone; point out the dullness of the sky.
I must wash the dishes, dry the plates, watch the TV by myself.

So now that you are dead my sweet, so now that you are dead,
I will catch the bus alone, sit with the strangers.
So now I will trudge, dazed, down the road to work where
I will sit by the phone.
Never again a call from you.

So now that you are dead my precious, so now that you are dead,
I will talk to your pillow as he wipes my tears away.
In sleep stretch out, only to find your place empty.

So now that you are dead my love, so now that you are dead,
I will visit you only in dreams; wish I had gone instead . . .

Negar Pashazadeh (17)
Cardinal Pole RC School

MY DAY: THE TOOTHPASTE

Nothing to say, nothing to do,
We were all bored, not just me and you.
The day had been a bore; the day had been a waste,
Until Daddy slipped on a tube of toothpaste!

We all laughed, we all smiled,
It seemed as if the day had been worthwhile.
I ran to get the camera. Clickety-click.
Daddy was so stupid; he fell like a brick.

Mummy came in, looked on angrily,
After a silence, she smiled with glee.
Daddy sat there, covered in paste,
When he tried to get up with too much haste.

It was great; it was fun,
On the day that Daddy fell on his bum!

Carl Hazeley (13)
Cardinal Pole RC School

TOM'S POEM ON LIFE!
(Reflections on 'The Glass Menagerie' by Tennessee Williams)

'Rise and shine, rise and shine!'
Mother's voice burns my mind
A twisted tale this tale of mine
Of a crippled kid and too much wine
I've drunk so much the words get slurred
To escape the Earth just like a bird
My father did, he left us all
Divided we stood, together we fall
My life's a puzzle incomplete
Mum controls us like a freak
Sister alone in her fantasy world
Remaining always as a little girl
For every day and every week
My eyes bleed tears which cannot speak
So rise I shall but I won't shine
The sun it shines with light that blinds
My heat is lost, heart cold as stone
I'll leave them both, even my home
I will not shine but yes, I'll stand
Alone in time like grains of sand.

Antronella-Marie Book (16)
Cardinal Pole RC School

I WANDERED LONELY AS A CLOUD

I wandered lonely as a cloud,
Through Manhattan, amongst the crowd.
This time last year, a solemn place,
Widespread grief throughout the race.
Dampened spirits held heads high,
Global warning - we will not die.
A self-inflicted pain? Who knows.
The truth will never be told my foes.
The wound will heal, but the scar remains,
Tempers flare like raging trains.
The solution is an awkward one,
When action's taken, you cannot run.
As the wrath of the world is eager to succeed,
Your sorry game is sure to bleed.

The tower inside us beats consistently, like the irregular sense of
Dickenson
They say this place will never be the same . . . I agree, it will be better
soon.
Their emotions vary from highs to lows,
This is the life they lead, but by no means chose.
The moon still shines - gives rays of hope
And when the sun shall rise - we are sure to cope.
Our spirits will be piecing the skyline, standing proud,
As high as our loved ones, up in the lonely cloud.

Stephen Charles (18)
Cardinal Pole RC School

THE SILENT SNIPER

He crawls along the forest floor
A match grade barrel to do his chore
Blending with the woodland scene
He leaves no trace of where he's been.

A single task occupies his mind
To the outside world he is blind
One single task, one single goal
Only his mission occupies his soul.

He moves into the open grass
The enemy patrol makes a searching pass
Although they, they cannot see
The man moving out from a distant tree.

One hour, two, three then four
He only moves a few feet more
Zero hour is getting near
He knows his target will soon appear.

A single man he has been sent to kill
And on his hands, this man's blood will spill
The moment is now, the target's in sight
Taking up the best position, the shot seems right.

One ounce more on the trigger sear
The bullet races away like a high-speed spear
It races through the air with a thunderous crack
There's a fountain of blood as it exits the man's back.

The silence is deafening, there's not a single sound
As the shooter removes the case of the single, spent round
His task now done, he fades back into the wood
His only trace is a body, where a man once stood.

Max Buadi (15)
Cardinal Pole RC School

BULLY

Everyone's scared of what I might do
I'm not what they see,
If only they knew.

They see an intimidating monster
Full of evil intent.
When really I'm kind
And that stereotype I resent.

Why do you look at me
And assume I'll lash out?
Why don't you get to know me
And realise what I'm about?
If you did you'd understand what
I'm going through.
A dysfunctional family,
Emotional distress
A victim of neglect
A cushion for violence.

So, is it a wonder
I wanna fight back!

Phoba Mbuli (15)
Cardinal Pole RC School

ANGER

All my blood is rushing around so fast,
I feel like shouting with a blast,
A teacher came, so at last,
I got in trouble, I am in a cast.
Now all the blood is in my feet,
I feel like giving those girls a beat,

Hallowe'en comes, trick or treat,
I can't wait to go to the hospital for a comfortable seat.
Now everyone is watching me,
I am looking around, I am feeling dizzy,
My head is getting fat and getting heavy,
I can't even watch any TV.

Leon Diamond (12)
Cardinal Pole RC School

TRUE LOVE

Everyday, of you I think
The many kisses and I sink
The strength to carry on my days
But with you my thoughts stay.
You are the raindrops
I am the sea
How beautiful it would be
If you were here with me.
Thy not try to win my heart
But virginity is what you want
Through passionate love
We would have fun
But love does not revolve
Around such things.
I still have my youthful beauty
In my soul shows deeper, beyond
My heart is what you shall win
And see the beauty of my skin.
In time love will show
My feelings grow
Then the birth of our child
From the beauty inside.

Kemelia Horne (15)
Cardinal Pole RC School

I THOUGHT YOU WERE DIFFERENT

(A response to 'To His Coy Mistress' by Andrew Marvell)

I thought you were different . . .
I really liked you as a friend,
But things didn't quite work out to be like that.
I thought you were different.
You told me that you would marry me
And maybe someday have kids.
I thought you were different . . .
We made a perfect couple.
People looked at us and adored us
As we walked by.
We used to lay down on the hot, sandy beach
Watching the sun go by.
I thought you were different.
I used to share my jokes and secrets with you,
But how can I trust you?
I thought you were different.
You are the same as the ones I have met and left.
You only wanted me in bed.
I can no longer look at your face,
You disgust me.
I thought you were different.

Whitney Johnson-Yeboah (16)
Cardinal Pole RC School

REMEMBER ME MOTHER?

Remember me Mother?
You said that you loved me
And you still gave me away.

Remember me Mother?
You said that you loved me,
Look at me now, you've left me here standing.

Remember me Mother?
No matter what you do,
I will always love you.

The mother I always needed but never had
Has run away and left me real sad.

Charlotte Desimone (12) & Lianne Cawley (13)
Cardinal Pole RC School

THE FANS

It was Friday night
The hall was packed
And they were chanting
The great one's name

The base itself was already taking over
The hall was vibrating and shaking
The people were feeling the vibes
They moved like ever

Atmosphere was lively
It was like the fans
Were in a hot frying pan
Waiting to be taken out

The rhythm fitted the place
At the time, the name
Was being chanted again

'Joel, Joel,' they said,
'We want Joel!' It was like
They were starving and
Couldn't be okay till
They had Joel for dinner.

Joel Adebayo (15)
Cardinal Pole RC School

HALLOWE'EN

The ghouls come out at night
And children wear silly costumes to fright,
But you know zombies are a terrible sight,
So why do you go out at night?

As the wind blows and twisters twist,
Witches' houses are full of mist,
Black cauldrons with stew in them,
Dead rats and bats, how can you miss them?

Ghosts play tricks on foolish children,
Eating candy stolen from Mother's kitchen,
But Hallowe'en is a celebration for ghouls,
Not silly children better known as fools.

Risha Parmar (11)
Chingford School

LONELINESS

She was a lonely girl.
She never had any friends.
Always on her own.
She even didn't know the meaning of friendship.
On her own all the time, in fact every break and lunchtime too.
How must she be feeling right at this moment?
Lonely as can be, but no one cares.

No one loved her, not even her frog.
What horrible days went by until . . .
One day she disappeared
Out of sight forever, never to be seen again.

I wonder where she may be?

Sanna Saeed (15)
Chingford School

DESARSTA WEDDING

'Ello, 'ello, R U der?
I can't believe I saw 'er underwear,
I woz sittin' 'ere, bored as hell,
Den I heard an almighty *yell*,
She'd slipped right over on 'er bum,
I thought, oh my god, what have I done?

She tripped cos of my toy truck,
At da moment I think she's stuck,
'Er dress is budged b'tween da stools,
I think I've broken all da rules.

She's lookin' at me wiv a nasty glare,
I smile back in hope and prayer,
I wonder if she can forgive me,
Cos dis wedding is so lovely.

Oh no, she's drawing near,
I am trembling wiv fear,
I can't believe what I've done,
Never mind, it woz loads of fun.

Jo Southwell-Sander (12)
Chingford School

GOING ON HOLIDAY

Smooth beach, sand against your feet, with the sea coming in,
And seagulls flying round you when you've got fish and chips,
And when you're eating ice cream, the sun melts it,
But on holiday you have the best time of your life,
And at night you have as much alcohol as you can get in.

Laura Goode (12)
Chingford School

FRIENDS

F avourite friends are all of you, I find it hard to get the same ones
like you.
R emember we are friends. Don't let that slip your mind.
I will always remember you, no matter what.
E nemies we were once in our lifetime, but we are still friends.
N umbers of times I've said I don't want to be your best friend.
D amn! I wish I could take that back, but all I can say is . . .
S orry, my friends. Please forgive me.

Stephanie Hughes (12)
Chingford School

HAPPY

I don't know how I feel,
I think I feel like an orange peel,
No I don't, I know how I feel,
I feel like writing a holiday report,
Well, that's what I thought,
I feel like playing with my mates,
But they're all out and about,
I know, it will count.

Blake Lewis (12)
Chingford School

DESERTION

He watched the snow fall and settle
As he waited for you
And then the snow melted away
With his dreams of you

But if he died at twelve tomorrow
Would you shed a tear
Or would you cry, but inside
Be acting insincere?

James Wright (14)
Chingford School

THE PARK

In the park we always have fun,
In the summer we catch the sun,
We sunbathe there for hours,
Just sitting around the flowers,
Having water fights,
Playing with our kites,
Whatever we do we always have fun!
Just sitting there in the sun.

Rochelle Harp (12)
Chingford School

WINTER

Winter is when it's so cold you wear gloves and scarves
Winter is when all it does is rain and all everyone does is complain
Winter is when you have that Christmas feeling wheeling down you
Winter is when it snows and everyone goes, 'Let's build a snowman!'
Winter is not summer, you don't get a tan
Winter is not summer when you boil in a frying pan
Winter is just cold.

Maria Constantinou (12)
Chingford School

LIFE WILL START AGAIN

In the forest we see life,
the trees, the leaves, the animals, they fight,
but in the end they will die
and life will start again.

In the sky the sun shines bright,
the bees and birds all take flight,
but in the end they will fall
and life will start again.

Finally there will be
no birds or bees that we can see,
or trees and leaves to grow again,
because the world will die out
but life shall start again.

Matthew Gregory (12)
Chingford School

THE EXQUISITE ICE CREAM

The fluffy white cream, like clouds,
and smooth and ice-cold.
Crumbly chocolate flake,
chocolate sprinkles or hundreds and thousands.
It's expensive money,
but it has sweet strawberry sauce.
The happy smiles,
the sunny days,
everyone happy and gay.

Jordan Wilson (12)
Chingford School

THE OBSERVER

Why are you here? Where are you going?
What is the point of your meagre existence?
Ev'rybody to-ing and fro-ing,
Tight-roping actions in the great balance.

The truth? But why would you want the truth?
Human beings are such petty creatures,
The enigma of life, just a roof
To house our suspicions of life's features.

As Shakespeare put it - players on stage,
He forgot to add - actors without direction,
Your life demonstrates G-d's great rage,
Pointless, precarious, per-hellish-dition.

Black awaits you in the approaching future,
Everything unforeseen and unforetold,
Life-post-death, who knows? Adventure
Or nothing, nothing to religion, stories old?

What can you do now to really live?
Use your ticking life-clock to the fullest,
What can you do? Actually give
Back to society to reach its summit?

Society? What's your reason for that?
Man-made creation, your path to destruction,
Rules by which you live, imposed boundaries, accepted fact,
Your safeguard and way to utter corruption.

For you are your own worst enemy
And you are only but a fruitless shell,
The pleasures of life drowned in a depthless sea,
Of greed, selfish men, you know you are, you tell.

Samuel Landau (14)
City Of London School

MY MOTHER

When she sings, she's like a train on fire,
Her curly hair and large mouth mean something dire,
She's an opera singer, you should know,
She opens her mouth with a terrifying blow.
The songs she can sing fill the church with noise,
When she talks on the phone, it even scares boys!

Her massive figure barges through crowds,
Her stomach loves food - she can eat mounds!
She may sound dumb,
But not to me,
And that's because
She's my mum!

Daniel Ong (11)
City Of London School

HOPE IS WHAT YOU MAKE OF IT

Hope is what you make of it.
If you want something, have hope,
But not too much, only a bit.
Because if it doesn't go the way you want,
You'll be disappointed,
Then you'll give up hoping, but you can't,
You'll still have hope somewhere in your heart.
And if it doesn't go the way you want,
Try to have a fresh start,
Have hope,
Even if you don't want to accept it,
Sit and use your wit,
And it'll eventually work out bit by bit.

Maryam Khazaei (15)
Clapton Girls' Technology College

MY TIME

(Based on 'Leisure' by William Henry Davies)

What is this life if full of care,
I have no time to stand and stare.

I have no time to look for my cat,
I have not even time to look under my mat.

I have no time to play with friends,
Not even to know what lies within them.

I have no time to hug or kiss my dad,
Not even to see him when butterflies fly past.

I have no time in this good life,
So enjoy it if you can and if you might.

So what is this life if full of care,
I have no time to stand and stare.

Susan Roberts (12)
Clapton Girls' Technology College

CAN SUCH BEAUTY BE TRUE?

His eyes glow like crystal balls.
His smile lights up my whole universe.
His is the warm sun in my summer day.
His is the beautiful white snow during winter nights.
He makes me laugh during my sad day.
He gives me strength when in I need it the most.
If he was to leave me it could be the destruction of my whole world,
But I always wonder could such beauty be true?

Andrée Wohi (14)
Clapton Girls' Technology College

LOVE, LUST OR AN INFATUATION?

I love you.
Well, at least I think I do
How am I to know whether it is love, lust or a teenage infatuation?

Is it love when we have stolen moments in a dark room,
with nothing but streaks of moonlight falling upon us
and illuminating your golden brown hair?

Is it love when you kiss me passionately,
when your tender hands caress me gently,
when you enclose me within your strong, masculine arms
and whisper sweet nothings in my ear?

I love you.
Well, at least I think I do
How am I to know whether it is love, lust or a teenage infatuation?

Is it love when I feel as though I'm on cloud nine whilst with you,
when, for the briefest moment in time;
I forget all about the downsides of life?

Is it love when we brush shoulders against one another,
yet we are not able to look at each other for a reason we know not of?

I love you.
Well, at least I think I do
How am I to know whether it is love, lust or a teenage infatuation?

Is it love when I can't get you out of my head,
when you constantly possess my thoughts,
whether it is before I go to bed, after I wake up and in-between the two
- in my precious dreams?

Is it love when I compare every man against you,
yet no man manages to match up to you?

I love you.
Well, at least I think I do
How am I to know whether it is love, lust or a teenage infatuation?

Is it love when all my thoughts fly out the window
every time your handsome face looks my way?

Is it love when I stare at you in marvel from a distance,
and when you eventually catch my eye, my heart goes into overdrive
at a million beats a minute?

So, is it love, lust or an infatuation?

They say you know when you fall in love,
and I know that I have fallen head over heals in love with you.

Sameena Desai (15)
Clapton Girls' Technology College

HMM . . . SUBJECTS

Art is full of colours
English is to do with grammar
Maths, a number twister
Science mad like my *sister*
Go drilling with technology
Oh the *humanities!*
Be like a model in drama
Music takes your mind into a
Different world
Explore the world in ICT
Stop being *lazy* and start going to PE
The world is beyond your eyes in geography
RE religions you'll learn from
Around the world
That's nearly all the subjects that I
Can think of.

Nazma Begum Ali (13)
Clapton Girls' Technology College

THE CREEPY HAUNTED HOUSE

At the end of a creepy wood,
A spooky haunted house stood.
Shattered windows to dangling webs,
To where the ghosts sleep in their beds.
From the ugly witches with broomsticks and cats,
To the monstrous monsters under the mats.
When it was first seen after 1000 years,
The visitors left in terrified tears.
Visit this creepy place if you dare,
But I warn you, you'll truly be in for a scare!

Tasneem Mithawala (11)
Clapton Girls' Technology College

FRIENDSHIP

You are my friend and I handle you with care
But all you do for me is give me a dare,
We all know that friends are rare
So now is the time for you to be fair,
I am telling you this because it's too hard to bear
So when you are ready I will be there waiting for you
To come and share.

Mumina Begum (11)
Clapton Girls' Technology College

SMILE

Smiling is infectious; you catch it like the flu,
When someone smiled at me today I started smiling too.

I passed around the corner and someone saw my grin,
When he smiled I realised I'd passed it on to him.

I thought about that smile and realised its worth:
A single smile, just like mine, could travel round the Earth.

So if you feel a smile begin, don't leave it undetected . . .
Let's start an epidemic quick and get the world infected!

Sharon Ogunbiyi
Clapton Girls' Technology College

WHO AM I?

Who am I?
I am the beauty of the green Earth,
and the angels among the sky,
I glow like a moon at night
and shine like a star in the morning,
I am the roots to every tree
and the petals to your favourite flowers,
I am the person who wipes your tears
and then slowly disappears,
I am the fire to your greatest desire,
who am I?
You'll find me in the rivers,
or maybe in the lakes,
you'll hear me and my flowers talk,
if you go on a nature walk,
you'll smell me in the binding air,
I'll always let you know I care,
you'll see me in your dreams,
when life's over it seems,
you'll taste me in your blood,
who am I?

Ebru Buyukgul (14)
Clapton Girls' Technology College

IS LIFE YOURS?

What is life
If you do not get a say in it?
How do you own something
But not own it?
You have a life
That is not in your control
But yet it is yours
Or is it?
Life belongs to your surroundings.
They say, when you cry, die and turn to ash.

My life has been taken from me,
I no longer have control
But did I ever have control?

From day one
I was forced to awake
With a slap to the bum.
At the age of nine
I was forced to play
With a slap to the head.
At the age of fifteen
I was forced to commit suicide
With a build-up of confused emotions.
Today
I was forced to say yes
With the aim not to hurt her feelings
But mine instead.
Nothing I have done in life
Has been done because I wanted to
Then again - it is what I expect
When you do not own your own life.

Bunmi Odubanjo (15)
Clapton Girls' Technology College

THE WEDDING

Today I'm being a bridesmaid,
I'm wearing a dress that's blue,
I've got a big bunch of flowers
And a pair of new shiny shoes.

Everyone's feeling excited,
It's such a wonderful day,
But why are both grannies crying
And what did Uncle Tom say?

The vicar was very boring,
Well that's what our dad said,
Mum said he should've whispered
And whacked him one on the head.

My auntie, the bride, looked so pretty,
It was fun when we had to sing,
But there was a big problem,
The best man said he lost the ring!

Later we all had a party,
And my mum and dad had a row,
Both the grannies were crying,
Grandpa was trying to fix his bow.

Everyone got rather tired,
The food and the drink were gone,
My flowers looked ugly,
The day had been very long.

I really loved being a bridesmaid,
It was such a wonderful day,
But I don't think I want to get married,
At least not in that way!

Ruhie Dyer (12)
Clapton Girls' Technology College

THE MAGIC BOX

(Inspired by 'The Magic Box' by Kit Wright)

I will put in my box...
The friendship that lasts,
Ancient history from the past
And the sound of a hot volcano ready to blast.

I will put in my box...
The snoring sound of someone sleeping,
A man sitting in his car beeping
And a shy little girl weeping.

I will put in my box...
The loudness of my party rockin',
The house keys lockin'
And the jingling sounds of my sweet stockin'.

I will put in my box...
A line from Shakespeare's books,
The beautiful pictures of Picasso's looks
And the dinner ladies that are the cooks.

I will put in my box...
The love and joy of my mum and dad,
My silly little brother being bad
And a sly green frog sitting on his lily pad.

I will put in my box...
My baby brother acting like a lad,
The sugary sweets that my sister had
And my downhearted friends feeling sad.

My box is fashioned with shamrock stones around the sides,
Also with a bright red rose in bloom.
The hinges are decorated with the fascinating dreams,
Wished by my family and me;
They are also covered with the bright shiny colours
From baby-blue to pink.

Inside it feels as smooth as a baby's bottom with soft lilac material.
I shall walk and glide gently down my box,
Flying around the world to see and find
More exciting things that I will add to my precious box.

Raj-Rani Kaur (13)
Clapton Girls' Technology College

AND THAT SOMEONE IS YOU

Once in a lifetime you meet
Someone very special
Who touches your life
In a very wonderful way.

Someone who makes you feel special,
Someone who makes you feel vulnerable,
Someone who makes you feel loveable,
Someone who makes you feel wonderful.

Someone who is always watching out for you,
Someone who is always thinking of you,
Someone who is always trying to protect you,
Someone who is always there for you.

Someone who you share your life with,
Someone who you share your happiness with,
Someone who you share your problems with,
Someone who you share your sadness with,
Someone who you share your love with.

And that someone is you,
Who makes me so wonderful.

Jahanara Begum (13)
Clapton Girls' Technology College

THE OLD DISCO GRANNY!

Two more steps she would have been a queen,
She had always shown off by making a scene,
She wouldn't stop no matter what,
There were even old men saying she was pretty hot.
Eleven years old she was when she took her first swing,
She was a dancer with the nickname Wild Thing,
Disco, disco, disco, that's what she loved,
People called her the disco dove.
Just around Christmas she became famous and bigger,
'Cause of her eating she lost her great figure,
She had five kids at a very early age,
Made it in magazines but people turned her page.
The years passed by, she became a great gran,
She also had been stalked by a psychotic fan,
Sold many dancing tracks, spent all her money,
Created a new move called dancing funny.
Then she realised that she was on her own,
Needed some money, had to sell her home,
After years and years of humiliation,
She became a joke for the entire nation.
She ended up living on a farm,
Cutting wood, she lost her right arm!

Hannah Adesanya (12)
Clapton Girls' Technology College

LIFE

Life is a maze through its twists and turns,
As most of us will sometimes learn,
That many a failure turned inside out,
From the good luck charm,
Till the clouds of doubt,
It feels like you are trapped in a den,
But trust me my friend you will win.

When things go wrong as they sometimes will,
When the right you're fighting for seems all uphill,
When debts are high and funds are low,
When we want to shine but we have to unglow,
When care is pressuring you down flat on your chest,
Rest if you must but try your best.

Fafali Jubey (12)
Clapton Girls' Technology College

OUR MIDGE (9.4.89 - 5.4.02)

She had a pedigree as long as your arm,
With fancy names from east and west,

But to us, she was a small brown cat,
With a big, big heart.

Not a snobby cat, with her nose in the air,
But a matey cat, with a friendly air.

Not a stay at home cat, with toes tucked in,
But an adventurous cat, with claws stuck out.

She chased off enemies with the best,
But mothered strays and welcomed guests.

At home in tents, caravans and boats,
Nothing phased her courageous soul.

She wasn't perfect, horrible habits tried our patience
And elicited curses from us all.

Our small brown cat with a big, big heart,
Our Midge.

Suzanna Hudson Cooke (12)
Clapton Girls' Technology College

LOST BACK HOME

Anxious, on a plane for the first time since I was two.
Bump, plane lands, head spinning, jet-lag.

So many new faces apparently aunts, uncles and cousins,
Driven to where I am to stay in a rickshaw rather slack,
I stare from face to face, trying to familiarise myself with them,
Close my eyes, trying to recall them, mind blank, everything black.

We sit and eat in a circle on the floor,
It is an important tradition here in Pakistan,
Trying to imagine what life is like here,
Sit and stare, looking for answers at the door.

Everyone's friendly, they want to talk to me,
Not knowing my language fluently, I stay silent, fearing humiliation,
I don't even know what type of people they are.

There's so much to tell them of my life in Britain,
I don't know where to start, I open my mouth,
My throat goes dry, unusual, I've drank loads of fluids,
Trying to ignore the excruciating heat unlike the rain
I'm more familiar with back home, where is my home?

I know they'd listen intently as they stare eagerly at my face,
Alien; I feel uncomfortable, looking at my parents for support,
But they are too busy engaged with family, glad to be united with.

TV, newspapers, cinema, bowling, shopping, Oxford Street, buses,
Unlike here, prayer, housework, prayer, rickshaws,
Market stalls selling cloth and tailors busy on sewing machines.

Having been to pilgrimage I feel so cleansed,
I feel more aware of time passing by,
I look ahead, what will the future hold, but now with no fear.

Sima Yousaf (15)
Clapton Girls' Technology College

How Do You Feel?

How do you feel?
How do you feel in the morning?
How do you feel in the morning when you look out of the window?
How do you feel in the morning when you've looked out of the window
and noticed it's pouring?

Your uniform hung out on the line
Just been soaked!
Your dog thought it would use your homework book as a chewing toy,
All you can say is, *'You stupid dog.'*
And all he can reply is, *'Woof, woof.'*
Your mum's shouting down your back and your sister just poured
orange juice down your school shirt.

School starts in ten minutes,
Another late and you've got detention,
It's best you hurry up and straight out of that door you go.

I tell you how I would've felt,
I would've felt like it's a new day,
Sun shining, the whole lot,
But then the clouds burst and start to pour rain, and that's the start
of a terrible day.

And I'll tell what I would've done, I would've
Kicked myself for hanging my uniform outside,
I would've strangled that dog!
And given my sister the whole lecture, get ready, then out of that
door and off to school.

And if the teacher did ask why I'm late I'll just hand her this poem
And say, 'It explains my situation, with my
Guardian/parent consent and signature below.'

Yvonne De Graft-Hammond (15)
Clapton Girls' Technology College

I Am A Star

I am a star who says hello to you.
I am a star which brightens you up.
I am a star up in the sky.
I am the star skating on the ice.
I am a star who will be with you every night.
I am a star who will say goodnight.
I am the star who says hello to the sun.
I am the star who looks after your life.
I am the star who looks after you.
I am the star far away from you.
I am the star that's silvery and bright.
I am a star who brings you love.
I am a star who brightens your life.
I am a star who twinkles at night.
I am a star shining in your heart.
I am a star who falls from the loving sky.
I am the star who brings you light.
I am the star you'll see every night.
I am a star who looks after you every night.
I am the star who brings love to your house.
I am a star who opens up your life.
I am the star up in the blue and dark sky.
I am a star who is so bright.
I am a star skating down from the sky.
I am a star looking over your house.
I am a star saying ta-ta.
I am a star who's grey and white.
I am a star up high in the bright dark sky.
I'm a star who says hello to the moon.
I am a star, a star so high up.
I am a star who's bright.
I am a star that can hear you when you cry.
I am something that lights the sky.
I am a star that watches you at night.
I am the star who lights the sky and it's bright.

I am a star who makes a pattern in the sky.
I am a wishing star
That brings anything to your life.
I am a star that you see.
I am a star who says goodbye.

Lumbardha Shabani (12)
Clapton Girls' Technology College

UNFAIR

It's not that easy being the middle child,
when your other brothers and sisters are either cute or wild.
It seems to you that your parents like them the most,
even in the morning when they give them the first batch of toast.

Walking from school slowly on your own,
thinking of new ways to persuade your parents for a mobile phone.
Everything you want to have they will say, 'No way!'
But when the others ask they will say, 'Okay.'

When you tell them the situation that they're putting you in,
there will be a huge reaction saying how you are lying.

On the next day you will have more attention,
but after a while you would have the same suspension.
Once again you're on your own, but you don't care,
you know how life is, life is unfair.

Yasmeen Varachhia (16)
Clapton Girls' Technology College

PARENTS

Parents are the ones that give you life.
Parents are the ones that take care of you.
Parents are the ones that love you.
Parents are the ones that comfort you.
Parents are the ones that tell you night-time stories
                                                when you can't sleep.
Parents are the ones that buy you clothes and gifts for birthdays.
Parents are the ones that make you laugh.
Parents are the ones that make you feel wanted.
Parents are the ones that help you with your homework.
Parents are the ones that understand what you're going through
                                                as a teenager.
Parents are the ones that get you out of trouble when you're a teenager.
Parents are the ones that give you a rise in your lunch money.
Parents are the ones that laugh at your jokes even if they
                                        don't like them.
Parents are the ones that take you to your friend's party to have
                                                a nice time.
Parents are the ones that make you a nice person.
Parents are the ones that think about you every night when you're
                                        out with your friends.
Parents are the ones that respect you.
Parents are the ones that teach you to cook dinner.
And if you say that you hate your parents and you wish they were dead,
Don't say that because some children like you need parents to love
                                        and care about you very much.

Naketa Burgess
Clapton Girls' Technology College

FIRST DAY IN SCHOOL

I was scared and thinking what the teachers would be like,
But then I sat on a chair, like it was my own bike.
The pictures on the wall reminded me of my pet
And the paintings children had drawn, reminded me of the kids
                                                    I hadn't met.
The alphabet on the wall gave me help to write a story
About a big man and his big lorry.

I looked outside; kids were playing in the playhouse
And one kid was sitting on the grass with a little mouse.
There were kids climbing on the climbing frames,
I wish I could call them, but I didn't know their names.

I went to the home corner, which was on one side,
I sat on the cushions trying to hide.
I didn't want to play,
But it was fun watching the kids all day.
I looked away and saw some books,
One of the books looked the way a cat looks.
There was a computer nearby,
There was even a kid trying to be a spy.

My teacher had the best chair
And the cushions on it felt like hair.
I used to sit on it when she didn't see,
So many things were near it, example - a picture of a tree.
The classroom smelt of milk,
The smell reminded me of silk.
My teacher's name was Mary,
She wasn't very scary.

Mahfuza Ferdous (12)
Clapton Girls' Technology College

ICE CREAM

I scream
You scream
We all scream
For ice cream!
A taste of heaven
On your tongue . . .
Ice cream land
Is where I belong!
Strawberry, chocolate
Vanilla too
All for me
None for you!

When on your face
You wear a frown
And you just feel
Upside down
Eat ice cream
And you'll feel happy
Wipe off that frown
As proven by me!
I scream
You scream
We all scream
For ice cream!

Tania Muhith (11)
Clapton Girls' Technology College

WHO AM I?

Who am I?
I wore glasses with elastoplast - pink frames
I had one foot three sizes larger than the other
I looked like no other
but it always seemed to bother.

Who am I?
I stood in the same room as you
I stood in the end of each line
when it was time for outdoor games.
I was always the last
I thought, that's okay. It will never happen again.

Who am I?
At play time it was always the same
I always wanted it to rain
so that the rain could take the pain away.
It was walking through the empty playground
that brought me to feel this way.

Who am I?
All I wanted was for you all to know my name
or just to look at me as the same
so this pain could go away.
Just one second to notice who I was.

Who are you? I am Tich Miller.

Precious Ugbomah (13)
Clapton Girls' Technology College

AFRICA

Africa is wonderful,
There's many sights to see,
You'll really enjoy it,
Especially the safari.

There are many countries in Africa
Such as Nigeria, Gambia, Mali and Togo.
There are many fruits in Africa
Such as pineapple, coconut and even mango.

Africa is beautiful,
It has a hot climate.
Just wait till you get there
It's totally great!

I've been to Africa,
I had a really good time.
I saw most of my family
And they were all fine.

So go to Africa,
Get away from this cold and wet,
Because if you go to Africa
It'll be an experience you won't forget.

Catherine Enilolobo (11)
Clapton Girls' Technology College

FLOWERS

Flowers, flowers growing everywhere,
All brightly coloured right over there!

Different types of flowers, all big and small,
Or even a chance of bulky and tall!

Round and fat, in the soil it's sat,
The dark brown soil is just like a mat.

Watered every day with a sprinkle of sunshine,
Come on everyone, it's time for fun time!

Sobia Khan (11)
Clapton Girls' Technology College

SUMMER

Summer is here so bloom away,
Winter is quite far away.
Autumn has done and gone,
Spring is a year away.

A mouse with a wheeze, a cough and a sneeze.
Winter brings sadness.

A duck with a nose as red as a rose.
Autumn is near.

A tiger with a tub full of cubs.
Summer is hot and bare.

A bear with honey, dull and funny.
Spring is sweet.

Summer is summer, a time for sunshine and sea.

Winter is winter, a time for frost and fright.

Autumn is autumn, a time for breezes and wind.

Spring is spring, a time for smells and hope.

Beauty Begum (13)
Clapton Girls' Technology College

HOPE

I wake up from a nightmare, hoping
I will see your face again.
I look in the mirror, hoping
I will hear your voice again.
I speak, hoping
I will touch your skin again.
I touch, hoping
I will reach your soul again.
I read our love, hoping
Our lips will touch again.
I sleep and dream, hoping
We will meet and sleep again
Every day.

Sebahat Akdogan (16)
Clapton Girls' Technology College

MY AMAZING BODY

I have an amazing body,
What's so smashing about it is my face,
It is the cutest face on Earth,
My hair is so long and pretty,
My hands they are so tender,
My legs have no spots and they are short,
My body has a good shape
And I love the way it is,
That's is what is so smashing about my body.

Tina Badaloo (13)
Clapton Girls' Technology College

I Need

I need . . .
A moment to unleash
A moment to be free
A moment to be somebody
I've always wanted to be
A moment to feel pain
A moment to feel love
A moment to share
With someone I love
A moment to see
Who I really am
All I need is a moment forever!

Rezia Khanom (12)
Clapton Girls' Technology College

My Sweetest Animal

My animal is the best.
My animal is the nicest.
My animal is the cutest.
My animal is a cat.
It's so soft I can't let go.
My cat jumps.
My cat flips.
The more he likes it the more he skips.
I like him too much, I can't let go
When my cat goes I'll be in tears.

Denisa Voka (13)
Clapton Girls' Technology College

WHAT IS LOVE?

What is *love?* I ask myself.

Is it something I have been forced to do for my whole life
Or is it another thing that every other teenager has experienced,
But fell out of?
As teenagers we are told that the only ones we're allowed to love
Are the chosen ones from God.
Hormones are racing, but what can you do?
The chosen ones have not yet been found.
In your dreams, you're strictly sure that your gift from God
Has just arrived,
But then something hits you that love is truly something
You would always find underneath your heart.

Rita Uyinmwen (15)
Clapton Girls' Technology College

THIS IS YOUR . . .

This is your special day,
This is the day when you feel a little bit older and wiser,
This is the day when you feel happy and excited,
This is the day when you share with your family, relatives and friends,
This is the day when you are a special person,
This is the day when you get lots of unwanted and useless presents,
This is the day when you get teased and told how quiet you were
as a baby,
This is your birthday.

Mumtaz Karim (13)
Clapton Girls' Technology College

LIFE

For some life is long,
For some life is short,
In the mission we have there's no time to abort.
The mission you start with is for you to choose
And the path that you follow will determine if you lose.
So choose the right path and go the right way
For our lives can end at any day.

Kotar Chelh (12)
Clapton Girls' Technology College

HOW MUCH DO I LOVE YOU MOTHER?

To explain how much I love you Mother
I would have to number the stars at night.
To tell you how comforting your touch is when I'm feeling down
I would have to watch the sun rise every day until I die.
To make you see how much you mean to me
I would have to fly out of this universe and back again one
thousand times.
To return the love you give to me
I would have to travel to the end of a rainbow.
Because nothing can replace you Mother
I have to protect you with my love.
Because you give love so easily
I have to give twice as much back to make up for it.
And because you are *my* mother
I must be the luckiest girl in the world
And for that I have to do nothing
Except love you from now until forever.

Jessica Verdon (14)
Connaught School For Girls

WATER

You wander like an angel in the sky,
When you are tired you climb down the fields
Like a wire to crack the hearts of every seed,
When you are shy you try every single colour
Like a circle in the sky,
Little drops in the eyes when a little baby cries,
A huge iceberg in the North Sea,
The biggest blue bed eyes can see,
Cold drink after a nice dessert,
A mirage to the lost ones in the desert,
Beautiful notes flying in the wind,
There isn't any fight you cannot win,
If you are angry you can be a dragon,
You are in England, in India, in Saigon,
No one on this Earth can refuse you or say no,
You are a gift, *thank you God.*

Serap Ihsan (14)
Connaught School For Girls

KNOCK DOWN GINGER

Knocking on the door, tap, tap, tip,
Running away, click, click, clicking.

Hiding in a bush, shush, shush, shush!
People coming out, 'Who's there? Who's knocking?'

Door closing, bang, bang, shut,
Coming out of bush, click, clack, snap.

Running away, click, click, click on an open pavement,
Lucky did not get caught! Let's do it again!

Christopher Davis (11)
Eastlea Community School

GROW UP LITTLE BOY

'When are you going to grow up?' they said.
I am too small for my age,
I can't do anything for myself.
They call me a 'midget',
They said I'm too small to play basketball.
Well, since you asked . . .
I wouldn't mind . . .
I wouldn't mind being a tree,
I wouldn't mind stretching my body,
Just to be a tree,
But if I can't be a tree
I would like to eat cake and baked beans
For breakfast, lunch and dinner,
If that will make me tall.
I would like to wear high-heeled shoes
So that I will be tall in front of people.
One thing I'd never like to be
When I grow up,
I'd never be a fat man
Who smiles with his fat cheek,
When he thinks he is running
People discover he's crawling,
He cannot fight and he's always late for lessons.

Franklin Folahan (14)
Eastlea Community School

FREEDOM IS FOR ALL!

They hunger for help in the lost world,
They looked for help but help never found them.
They sang for help but it never came.

Their feet were as dry as the dusty ground,
The word freedom dropped out of their mouths like rainfall.
They have no one to turn to but themselves.

The world looked as if it was coming to an end.
The leaves went all dry; their eyes went all hard.
It was frightening, they saw the food, but it could not be touched.

Their imagination is to live in a paradise,
Where there will be peace and happiness,
Sitting in their palace like a lion king,
They will treat their people equally,
They will feed their people till they burst.

They are talented in different ways,
They are eager for freedom,
They are ready to take all the risks they can.
They put God first in everything.
They sing the song of praise for freedom.

The chamber was dark and dirty,
The chains were the enemy holding them back.
The day came by and the night went past,
They lay on the floor like a lonely child.

They think about what the future holds for them.
What is there to tell their coming generation?
What is there to gain out of this criticism?
What is there to write about?

The call for help is still coming,
The call for freedom is still calling,
Freedom is for all.

Adeyemi Baba Tunde Selam (15)
Eastlea Community School

MY DAD

You!
Your head is as bald as a bowling ball.
You!
Your eyes are as dark as the night.
You!
Your mouth is as big as the Dartford tunnel.
You!
Your arms are as strong as an iron bar.
You!
Your hands are like spades.
You!
Your legs are as long as a broomstick.
You!
Your feet look like flippers.
You!
You're my dad and I love you.

Hayley Barnes (11)
Eastlea Community School

MY INSIDES STAY THE SAME

I don't understand why you treat me
The way that you do,
When all I do is listen to
Everything that's true.

You say that friendship's deeper
Than water, blood or pain,
But no matter how deep love goes
My insides stay the same.

I wish you weren't so shallow,
That you go beyond what you see
'Cause now I know I'm changing
But it's 'cause it pleases me.

So don't let appearances mislead you;
My outside's not to blame,
'Cause no matter how I change on the outside
My insides stay the same.

'Cause even though I'm changing
My insides stay the same.

Gina Langton (16)
Eastlea Community School

EASTER, WHAT IT REALLY MEANS

Easter is a time for giving out sweets and candy,
Chicks and bunnies representing the lies,
But what's all this got to do with what Easter really is?
Easter was the time after slaughter and pain,
Blood and lots of clothes' stains,
Easter is the time when Jesus Christ
Rose up from the cave in which he lay,
Sweets and candy? Chicks and bunnies?
All part of the conventional scam
To cheat people out of their money!
Is this what we've really come to?
Cheats, lies and all for nothing.

The true meaning of Easter Sunday
Will never be true again,
Times have changed, not for the best,
Now instead of Easter being about Jesus, pain and suffering
It's about candy and cute little animals.
The times are changing,
We are too,
Too many lies,
Too little truth.

If you like to vomit,
Tell lies not truth,
Do you like chicks and bunnies?
Easter is what it is today,
It's your problem, not mine.

Kelsey Christou 12)
Highams Park School

DESTROY

My mission is to destroy
Everything that comes my way,
I'd hoped it wouldn't come to this,
I'd hoped to be calm.

It all happened when I tried to help a stranger,
Someone who I had never seen before,
They betrayed me and I lost my nerve,
I'll never be the same again.
It has been three months since it happened,
I've never forgotten it for one second,
In one day, in one week, in one month,
That I had committed a crime.

A crime so dreadful
That I shudder to think about it,
A crime so terrible,
That wasted a life.

Sarah Jones (12)
Highams Park School

FRIENDS ARE . . .

Friends are loyal and true.
Friends help us when we are down.
Friends always have fun together.
Friends always have a laugh.
Friends always pig out on food!
Friends are always the ones to help you.
Friends go shopping with you.
Friends never let you down!
Friends will always be your friends
No matter what happens,
Because friends are your friends forever.

Rebecca-Anne Wren (12)
Highams Park School

WHAT WOULD HAPPEN?

What would happen
If there was thunder and the world was cast asunder?
What would happen
If there was no light and no bird took flight?
What would happen
If everything was fair and there was no need to share?
What would happen
If there was blight and everyone started to fight?
What would happen
If everyone was happy and no one felt crappy?
What would happen
If the world was not a snare and there was time to stop and stare?
What would happen
If I stopped right now and I never started again?

Qayum Mannan (12)
Homerton College Of Technology

THE GALAXY

The galaxy is full of stars and a moon,
If I was an alien I'd go there so soon.
Morning and night,
Don't forget noon.
My ride will be a hot air balloon,
If I chose a colour it would be maroon.
I would take my dishes and a spoon,
Not forgetting the TV to watch my cartoons,
If you would like to join me on my holiday to the moon,
Please reply back to be quick and soon.

Sonam Bhaat (13)
Joseph Clarke School

MISS RICHARD

In the morning I walk into school, I walk into the classroom,
I find a seat at the back row and sit down.
My teacher, Miss Richard, looks right at me with an evil face,
With spittle dribbling down her face like a filled milk pan that has been
overheated,
She advances on me,
'Where have you been?'
'Oh I'm sorry Miss Richard, but David keeps bullying me on the way
to school.'
'Well boy, *make sure it never happens again,* or else . . .'
And she stomps back to her desk muttering to herself about stupidity.

Then all is quiet.
I sit in the back and close my eyes.
I begin to daydream.
I am running, running so fast that the trees in the forest are rustling as
I race past.
But the problem is, I don't know why I am running.
I hear something in the trees so I jump behind a large
Beautiful tree and stay silent.
'I will smell you out.' Oh no it's Miss Richard!
What was that?
Wh . . . wh . . . what?
'How dare you? How dare you sleep in my class!'
And she goes on and on like an irritating bee.
Her spittle dribbling down her chin,
Her face twisted,
Her nose wrinkled,
Her fists out in front of her like a boxer
And even a large and disgusting bogey was snaking its way
Out of her nose into her mouth.

She did not care as she still bellowed on like a bursting balloon.
I just looked straight down, looked as if I was bored.
Soon she got bored of bellowing,
Stomped out of the classroom.
The whole class laughed.

Nadim Miah (14)
Joseph Clarke School

SOUNDLESS

Walking down the street,
Thinking who to meet,
See, look and hear,
Whispers far and near,
The moon is out,
The sun is in,
Who to fear?
No one's been,
Singing and whistling,
Who could it be?
Remember no one is seen,
Cars are passing by,
Aeroplanes are flying,
But there is still no sound,
That I have found.

Nafisa Hussain (14)
Joseph Clarke School

My Mad Mum

My mum loves her music
It's blaring night and day
I wish she'd use them headphones
To keep the noise at bay.

Our house it's like a nightclub
It's rocking with the sounds.
She thinks she is eighteen again
When she dances round and round.

The windows might start breaking
With all the noise she makes
Sometimes I have to shout at her
'Oh Mum, for heaven's sake!'

Her singing is atrocious
She sings so out of tune.
She couldn't live without it,
I think she is a loon.

It really makes her happy
So I guess it's not so bad
But nothing keeps her quiet
And I think she might be mad.

Craig Brett (14)
Joseph Clarke School

SLEEPING

We like dreaming,
Sometimes dribbling
In our sleep.
We fly in cars
Through the night air,
Blue clouds,
We pass gold stars,
Moving as fast as a cheetah.
Robots with flashing, sparkling lights,
Sweeping the ground with mechanical brushes
And firing themselves into space.
Streams of melting chocolate.
We dive into lakes of fizzing, swirling sherbet
And jump into piles of spilling, spinning sweets.
In our dreams
We fly to Disney Land,
Enjoy the rides.
We camp in caravans
And chalets.
In hot countries
We ski in Austria
On snowy mountain slopes.
Floating on the Atlantic Ocean,
Or sailing
Across an ink surface
To awake peaceful and calm.

Natasha Berry, Levi Johnson, Kasim Khan & Fleur Skinner (11)
Joseph Clarke School

TOGETHER

My mum's in the shower,
She wants to smell like a flower.
She's got a big date tonight,
She thinks she's found Mister Right!
His name is Pete,
He thinks he's real neat.
They ain't right for each other,
He's a real bother!
My mum thinks he's great,
How could he be?
He's thirty-eight.
Pete thinks she's great too,
But how could she be?
She's thirty-two.
They ain't gonna be together
And I'll make sure of that!

Aisha Begum (13)
Joseph Clarke School

THE CITY

A city is the place to be
You can be lively and free
You can live in gangster styles
But you can get onto police files
You can have houses or flats
And maybe a few cats
You can leave or stay
But make your own way.

Katie Brown (13)
Sarah Bonnell School

MY MUM

My mum is kind and lovable,
She loves me and my family,
She's caring and helps me in every way
She's my mum that's who she is
And I love her all the way.

My mum tells me what to do,
Teaches me the right way,
She tells me not to go the wrong way,
She explains to me what I do not know,
She talks about her past too.

My mum makes me laugh and everyone too,
She always has a smile when she's happy,
She gives us lots of presents and makes us happy,
She loves going out and having some fun,
My mum's always there to give us a hand.

My mum is great and incredible,
She doesn't work or go to school,
But works very hard in the house,
Cleaning, washing everywhere
And I help her with it too.

My mum teaches us our religion (Islam),
La-illa ha illa hu muhammadur rasul-ulla,
There is no God but *Allah* and Muhammad (SAW)
Is the messenger of Allah.
Which then I read in the books every day.

When my mum goes on holiday,
I miss her lots and lots
And when she's back,
With all the family,
My mum's always there to smile.

Saera Sulthana (12)
Sarah Bonnell School

LIKE MOTHER, LIKE DAUGHTER

Mum, you are
One of a kind
There is no other
I can find.

Mum, you're a
Role model to me
And you're always
There for me.

Mum, you are
My best friend
You're there when
I need to defend.

Mum, you help me
To learn
You also make
Me earn.

Mum, you set me
A good example
You taught me
Different samples.

Mum, you're really
Funny
You always make
The day sunny.

Mum, you expect
The best of me
That's why I love you
You see.

Mum, how I long to be like you
Because I love you too!

Priti Kukadia (12)
Sarah Bonnell School

TO MS CALHOUN, WITH KINDNESS

She's always nice
It never costs a price
She always smiles
And she's never vile.

She's always happy
Always bubbly
She's never down
It won't be nice if she had a frown.

She never shouts
It's very rare
But if she does
It gives you a scare.

She's got short hair
Quite fair
She's very kind
All year round.

Rosemary Godwin-Ese (12)
Sarah Bonnell School

SUMMERTIME

Summertime, it's so cool
Everyone needs a cold swimming pool
It's wicked
It's so fine
That's what it's like in summertime.

The red sun is hot and very bright
In summertime it's so light
Caps we need on top of our hair
Shorts and T-shirts is what we wear.

All the children run
When they hear the ice cream van
They play on the sand of gold
Which is very fun.

But behold
The wave is coming
So run, run, run.

Loatifa Khan (11)
Sarah Bonnell School

A SPECIAL M8

Blossom Girl I call her
The way she giggles, the way she laughs
Just by looking at her makes me laugh
When it comes to nails, no one's ever to touch them.

My friend is very sweet, everyone thinks she's really cute
On she puts, a bright pink lipgloss
At the end she leaves a sparkle
She has always been there for me, left a shoulder to cry on.

Great big hugs she gives me
Sometimes I feel so lucky to have her
I've had the best times with her
She is the bestest m8 I ever had and she always will be.

Rukshana Sultana (12)
Sarah Bonnell School

DEATH

The door opened and in walked Death
His clothes were as dark as a cave in the night
His eyes were colourless and dull
There wasn't a single speck of light in them.

His lips were as dry as the Egyptian desert
His nose was long and straight
But you couldn't see all of it
Because his black hood covered it.

His skin was as rusty as an old book
And as rough as a crocodile's body
His nails were pointy and sharp
As if he was saying I will get you.

He smiled a sneaky smile
When his disease spread around
Killing everyone in the room
In a nasty way.

He left the room with blood all over it
But he came back to say to the three children left,
'I may have not got you now, but I'll get you next time!'
And he slammed the door behind him.

Jasmin Ahmed (11)
Sarah Bonnell School

A POEM FOR SOMEONE SPECIAL

My mum fills the hole in my heart,
She cares for me and she loves me,
She's always there when I fall
And she's always there when I need her.

My mum is my role model
She says, 'I do everything for your sake,'
She makes me laugh,
She speaks four languages.

She supports me
She takes me shopping
She buys me lots of clothes
And she gives me lots of presents.

She tells me what's right,
Or what's wrong,
She always praises me,
She's very protective.

My mum's kind and helpful,
But she hasn't met her mum in four years,
Cause she wants to be there
For me every day.

I'm proud to be her daughter,
She's proud to be my mother,
I love her
And she loves me.

Serash Hussain (12)
Sarah Bonnell School

DARKNESS

The dark knight rode into the castle,
His fiery stallion brought in the night.
He snuck into my room through the window,
Without such a whisper or sight.

With a kiss he took away my beauty,
With a touch of his hand he stole my youth.
He used night's dark power to cast a spell,
And captured my soul with his heart.

When morning's first light touched my window,
Full of sadness was my mind.
When morning's first light touched my window,
He took everything else he could find.

When the mist had risen and blown away
And the world was born anew,
Gone was he with the moon and stars,
His fading words, 'Adieu fair lady, adieu.'

Leaving the castle empty,
Silent, like the loneliness that lives inside of us.
Fair lady I was no more,
My silver hair about me,
A faded gown with faded memories,
Never to be told again.

No one was left to see the tears fall,
Down my furrowed face,
Only the spiders left to hear
My final dying grace.

Isabella McAdam (15)
Sarah Bonnell School

FOR SOMEONE SPECIAL

My dad is loving
But also caring
Over-protective
But always kind

Gives me presents
Gifts, clothes, jewellery
My dad is funny
Makes me laugh with jokes

Expects the best from me
Behaviour
Courtesy
And good grades

Loves me over anything
Gives me plenty of pocket money
Which makes my smile
Come alive

Works over the top
To make everyone happy
Doesn't have a job now
But still works hard.

Vaishali Patel (12)
Sarah Bonnell School

MY WONDERFUL MUM

She goes to work day in, day out
To be face to face with people who shout
She's a manager who's tough
So fast, so quick, so buff

She's always smiling and never down
Anyway, it doesn't suit her when she frowns
My mum is so caring
When I'm in a race she's always there cheering.

Janine Murrell (12)
Sarah Bonnell School

I'M PROUD TO BE HER DAUGHTER

I'm proud to be her daughter,
She's proud to be my mother.
She loves me more than anything
And I love her too.

She cares for me a lot,
She's very protective too.
She always wants to see me happy,
I hope she's happy too.

My mum is very beautiful,
Funny, smart and intelligent.
She listens and understands me,
She's always there for me.

My mum wants me to work hard,
She expects me to achieve high.
She helps me with my homework,
'Never give up,' is what she says.

My mum is always right,
She just can't be wrong and that's why,
I'm proud to be her daughter,
For there is no one like her.

Yosheeta Gunamal (13)
Sarah Bonnell School

MUM

She fills the hole in my heart
and she works very hard.
She is my role model
and she will always catch me when I fall.

Talk about working hard,
how can she live with me and my sister
arguing and fighting?
She must be super mum
especially when she comes back from work
but it doesn't bother her that much
because she loves us all
me, my sister and my dad.

She spoils me when I'm good
and she praises me
and she also sets me a good example
of course she does that
that's what mums do
but my mum is special.

My mum went through pain just to have me
I love her very much
and no one can come between me . . .
and my mum!

Chelsea Gromet (12)
Sarah Bonnell School

FRANKIE

There is a girl called Frankie,
Who's real popular in the school.
She wears proper nice clothes
And doesn't act a fool.
The girl is always smiling
No matter what the mood,
Her nails don't need filing
And she is never rude.

Frankie is like a sister,
Helps me when I'm down,
Lifts me off my feet
And never shows me a frown.
She talks to me and listens,
No matter what I say,
Even if I'm talking gibberish,
We talk, it ain't child's play.

And one last thing I would like to say
About the girl I'm writing about,
She's probably a role model
To nearly all the girls in my school.
She doesn't need to shout,
As she's really pretty and really hard to miss,
The girl is so intelligent,
The girl's extra bliss!

Stephanie Gharu (12)
Sarah Bonnell School

FOR SOMEONE SPECIAL

You are so beautiful; I love you with all my heart
You are always there when I need you in my life
You play a special part
You always make me smile when I am sad
And tell me off when I am bad
I am lucky to have somebody like you
Because you will always love me no matter what I do
I think you are really sweet and also kind
And you also have a brilliant mind
You! This special person I am talking about is not someone
Who is known to scream and shout
But you are a person who likes to keep things to themselves
And you really like to have a lot of wealth
So you, this person I am talking about, is the person
That makes me dance and hum
Who else could it be than my darling, caring mum.

Pearl Egbaran (12)
Sarah Bonnell School

A SPECIAL POEM FOR A SPECIAL SOMEONE

When I'm rude you just ignore it,
I'm your eldest and stubbornest child
I'm spoilt and a brat
But you always try not to give a bad reaction
I'm a brat and never will I change
But you just listen and watch how I grow to be . . .
Different day by day.

Raeesa Karim (12)
Sarah Bonnell School

ME AND MY BROTHER

When I am in my deepest dream
My brother is up to some type of scheme
I wonder why my brother has to lie to me
I'll let him off, I'll let him be.

My brother is as tall as a giraffe
When I look up all I see is his warm, fluffy scarf
Compared to him I'm really small
Hey! What can I say, my brother's tall
While he plays on his PS2 I haven't a clue what to do
There's only a couple of words to describe my brother
He is a tall, lean, lying machine and doesn't give a bother.

Gabriella Melin (11)
Sarah Bonnell School

TO MUM

My mum is very caring, but also very daring
She makes me laugh, she makes me cry
She fills the hole in my heart
But also she is very special to me.

My mum never gives up
If she wants me to do my best
She tells me that I am the best,

My mum also tells me
That I need to try my hardest in life to get far
She also makes me smile, that is worth the wait.

Anam Hussain (12)
Sarah Bonnell School

WAYNE

When I'm upset he makes me happy
I can trust him to stand up for me
When I'm in trouble he is always there for me
And he smells very nice
When it's my birthday he takes me to dinner
And we dream of each other every night
He is so quiet and he is tough
He is so funny, he makes me laugh.
He has friends who are very nice
But he will always be the best.
He acts like a gentleman when he's around me
He buys me presents like I do for him
We will always love each other forever.

Karla Thomas (12)
Sarah Bonnell School

A POEM FOR SOMEONE SPECIAL!

My friend really cares for me
and is very thoughtful
as well as wonderful
she's funny as well as childish
she gives me protection
and a lot of affection.

She likes Hindus' rights
and is very bright
she's always in my sight
and is ready for a fight
she's just like sunshine
even when the rain's pouring down.

I know I can trust her
as she's very sweet
just like a treat
she's there when I need her
so she's never too far
and is known as a fantastic star.

Chandni Dattani (12)
Sarah Bonnell School

MY MUM

My mum is loving and caring
Helping and laughing
Always helping me with my homework
And she loves to be happy.

She expects the best from us
And always says work hard and try your best
When we were small she taught us to tie our laces
She always has a smile on her face.

On my birthday
She gives me presents
She loves to make her children happy
And makes us delicious food.

I am proud to be her daughter
And she's proud to be my mother
She gives all her love to us
And we give her all our love.

Nishitha Sadiqe (12)
Sarah Bonnell School

Ms Colhoun

Ms Colhoun is a role model
She makes fun when she teaches
She makes a joke out of it
She's very kind and loving
Thank goodness I got Ms Colhoun as my English teacher.

Ms Colhoun it not an ordinary teacher
She is better and acts our age
To me Ms Colhoun is like big sister
And is always there to hear your problems
And knows what's best for us as our teacher.

Ms Colhoun is very pretty with her everyday smile.

Stephanie Drummond (12)
Sarah Bonnell School

I'm The Best Student

I ripped up my homework
And put it on the teacher's desk
She gave me an A and said
It was my best!

I called my maths teacher a ferret
She said I was too kind
So she gave me a merit!

I think I'm allergic to my teacher Ms Daisy
Because she makes me sneeze like crazy!

Fhathema Akther (11)
Sarah Bonnell School

ONE DAY

One day my husband went to war,
I'd never felt so much pain before.
The day he left I cried and cried,
Not knowing how I would survive.
Then I was told that he had died,
The grief I felt was hard to hide.
My mom was there, she held me tight,
Telling me that I'd be alright.
She said strength was all I had to find,
I knew I had to take my time,
Because the love I once had was hard to find.

Leigh Suzan Donovan (15)
Sarah Bonnell School

WRITE STUFF

Women are, women are, women are
Woman are weak
Women are gentle
Women are kind, women aren't mental
Women have friends
Women drink wine
Women are loving and are always fine
Women give hugs
Women are geeks
Women are, women are, women are weak
Women are touchy
Women aren't rough
Women always like romantic stuff.

Esma Savas & Sara Riahi (13)
Skinners Company School For Girls

WRITE STUFF
(Inspired by Michael Rosen)

Right Class 6
Right Class 6
I'm talking
I'm talking
I want complete quiet . . . and that includes you David Alexander
Yes you!
No need to turn around David, there aren't any other David Alexanders
here are there?
Louise, is it absolutely necessary for your watch to play London's
Burning just now, is there?
Right, as you know it was our plan to go out today to the . . .?
Science Museum, yes, that's it.
Now I had hoped that it wouldn't be necessary for me
to have to tell you . . .
Yes, you as well, Abdul, you're in Class 6 as well, aren't you?
I saw that Mark, I saw it. Anymore and you'll be out. No trip, nothing.

Zeba Ghanchi (11)
Skinners Company School For Girls

WRITE STUFF

Always do the write stuff
Don't punch me in the belly
You'll give me a tummy ache
Don't slap me on the head
You'll give me a headache
Don't punch me on the tooth
You'll give me a toothache
You've made me feel miserable
You've made me feel scared
You're not doing the write stuff!

Gulay Bulut (11)
Skinners Company School For Girls

WAR

9/11 was a tragic day
no one knew what to say
tears are falling down your face
war everywhere, it's a disgrace.
World War I was bad enough
and then came World War II that was tough
bombs can fall on your home
sometimes when you are all alone
you don't know what to do
all you can do is just sit there, just lonely you.
Just waiting for Mum and Dad to come through the door
alas, she knows they may have been killed in the war
she wonders if her family is going to be long
but yet she knows something's wrong.
She waits and waits, but no one comes home
and there she is, left all alone.

Jennifer Murphy
Skinners Company School For Girls

RIGHT STUFF

R   ight stuff is not doing the wrong stuff
I   t is working hard at school
G   oing the wrong way means failure, it's
H   ard to always do the right stuff
T   rying hard becomes the best.

S   aying please and thank you
T   ry, try, try and
U   will become the best
F   ailure is horrible
F   riends and family are always there, respect that.

Abigail Campbell (12)
Skinners Company School For Girls

WRITE STUFF

My dad is a rock and roller,
My mum is a disco queen.
Brother Itfaq's a crazy drummer,
He's the wildest that you've seen.

Sister Ruby is a singer,
With our cousin Fatima Ali;
Uncle Fiaz, well he's a showman,
There's not much that he can't do.

Auntie Yasmin is a cowgirl,
Grandpa plays a mean guitar,
Grandma is an opera singer,
Now she's terrific - what a star.

Every week we get together,
Man we really have a ball.
And me? I'm just a brand new baby,
But I'm the loudest of them all!

Aashia Azam (13)
Skinners Company School For Girls

WRITE STUFF

Wrong or right, it's the best
Rich, creamy, black or brown, it's beautiful
I love it, so do my friends
The best thing about it is when it melts in your hands and you can lick it
Everyone adores it, even teachers too (unbelievable!)
Sticky and sweet just the way I like it
Too many of them rot your teeth

Who cares!
Usually I get ten packs of them
Two every day, Monday to Friday
Fun for parties, even for a normal play
Flippin' heck, it's only chocolate . . .
(But who cares, I love it!)

Parminder Pathore (11)
Skinners Company School For Girls

THE BULLY

I see him in the playground
  He's coming over to me
    I know what he might do
      I'm scared of what it might be

He may trip me over
  As I'm playing games
    Steal all my school money
      Call me horrible names

But there's nothing I can do
  Because I'm weak and small
    But he is more the opposite
      Big, lean and tall

But me, why me?
  What did I do anyway
    Is it because I'm smart?
      Is this why I'm bothered all day

But soon I'll put a stop to it
  All this horrible hate
    Smarty-pants, four-eyes
      Oh well, too late!

Yemi Ajayi (12)
Skinners Company School For Girls

THE PAIN OF WAR

Children screaming and crying because they are burnt
War is a lesson that will never be learnt.

Mothers watch their children die
Fathers watch their wives cry.

A bomb falls from the sky so very fast
And hits the floor with a tremendous blast.

The agony sweeps in the atmosphere
For all the people that stand so near.

People lose arms, people lose legs
But none are as worse as the people who are dead.

People see something fall from the sky
Then they blast into oblivion in the blink of an eye.

Babies and children all alone
Sit in a corner without a moan.

Children starving, poor and in pain
All they want is food, just a single grain.

We need to think of other people and not just ourselves
When all these people act and feel like they are in prison cells.

While you sit down in your nice warm home
Just think of these people who are cold and alone.

Sarah Kotb (13)
Skinners Company School For Girls

THE RIGHT STUFF FOR SCHOOL

For what is right, I long
Shunning all that is wrong
With the right stuff for school
I'm more likely to keep calm and cool.

The attitude I like to find
Is the clear thought of a studious mind
I need to feel the genuine elation
From an hour of decent education.

The right stuff I seem to lack
Is to keep my time keeping on track
It's really great, when I'm not late
Late marks on the register is the thing I most hate.

The right stuff for us to wear
Avoiding the unwelcome stare
Is uniformly black and red
Colours of which some pupils dread.

The right gear and the right books
Good company and the right looks
Smart shirts and sensible shoes
Belongings that one does not lose.

Though to such rightness I aspire
I do not always attain this desire
Let knowledge and virtue grow
These are the rightest things I know.

Yumna Ahmed (13)
Skinners Company School For Girls

MR WRITESTUFF

He did the write stuff at the right time and at the right place
And always put a smile on my face
He was Mr Writestuff and to me that's no bluff.

Whenever I was sad he was always by my side
He always saw right through me and so there was no need for me to
hide even when I tried
To decide things that were private or classified
I know that he would always love me, no matter what I did
Even though in his eyes I was still a kid.

He did the write stuff at the right time and at the right place
And always put a smile on my face
He was Mr Writestuff and to me that's no bluff.

For me he was always my Mr Writestuff
He always did the best he could
Even though I knew he would
He knew so much that he reminded me of a child prodigy
To come so near and yet so far
I believe he is within me like a guiding star
Reminding me of what's right and wrong.

So, thank you Lord for bringing such a great man into the world
I just hope he knows that I am a very lucky girl
To have had a 'gracious grandad'!

Sonia Ahmed (14) & Jaskiran Kaur (13)
Skinners Company School For Girls

WRITE STUFF

On Hallowe'en Mum and I made a pumpkin lantern
Huge, triangular eyes and a square nose
It cried when we dug out its pyramid teeth
'Ouch!' it said, 'this is worse than the dentist!'
I got a fright, but the strangest thing was my mum didn't hear it
'Dentists at least give gas,' pumpkin complained
There was my mum oblivious, still hacking out its brain
'Come on, dig in,' she said, 'this is taking hours, it'll turn back
into a carriage!'
I started feeling dizzy, giddy, all out of sorts
I tried to hold its jaw closed so it couldn't talk
'Ouch!' it said, 'my chest bone, do I have to be hollow?'
'Of course you do,' I whispered, 'this is All Hallow's Eve.
We will put a candle in the hollow.'
'Oh no,' screamed pumpkin, 'I am going to burn my skull, worse than
Catherine.'
Suddenly Pumpkin rolled off the table
'Look what you've done!' shouted Mum. 'You careless thing!'
'It wasn't me,' I said breathlessly and pleased
Pumpkin was trying to escape
'Oh for goodness sake,' said Mum. 'What's the matter with your head?'
'It's not her head,' pumpkin said, 'it's mine! I've got a dreadful
headache. Got anything for it?'
But Mum, who heard Pumpkin's piercing voice, fainted, falling into
the basin with all the apples looking
If you want to do the right stuff, do it kindly, gently and slowly
without rush and you will succeed and if you can't do it keep trying
and don't give up.

Bukola Olayemi (11)
Skinners Company School For Girls

153

TEACHERS WHO DON'T UNDERSTAND

'Why can't you hear, just stop talking,' they scream
Millions of teachers around the land
'You are talking too loud, be quiet and listen,'
Teachers just don't understand.

They don't understand how interesting it is
To hear the latest gossip from your friend.
They stop you halfway through, then send you outside
So then you can't hear the end.

They don't understand why we're chewing
Chewing up green bubblegum
They tell us to put it in the bin
On the way it gets stuck to their bum.

They don't understand why our coats are on
It's winter and it's really cold
They say, 'I'm not cold and look what I'm wearing.'
That cos they're 40 years old.

They don't understand the way we are
Talking, chewing, coats on, what a strife
But we're the wonderful kids of the millennium
And that's just life.

Fiona Daly (13)
Skinners Company School For Girls

WRITE STUFF

Write what you think is right
And stand up for your rights
When you write what you think is right
Then be proud to write your rights!

Charelle Samuels (11)
Skinners Company School For Girls

THE WRITE STUFF

We enter the darkness all tattered and scared
What do we see, nothing but an old rusty chair
We walk on and on still we hear trees
But there is something coming between my knee
What shall I do? Should I jump and shout or dance about?
What could it be? Someone please help me
But I still carry on seeing as everyone has gone
There is someone, who can it be?
My aunt, my uncle, sshh who can it be?
Superman/Batman or maybe a chimpanzee?
I hope he/or she can help me
The next minute I hear a sound, who can it be?
The butcher/ baker or maybe the candlestick maker?
Then I begin to hear, 'Levi, Levi!'
I get up for school, oh well.

Levi Hawe (12)
Skinners Company School For Girls

LIVING

L   iving, oh living, I am living in a world of sin, but I hope tomorrow
     will be better.
I   wish that the world was good. Oh look what the Lord God has done
     for us. I am just living in a world of sin.
V   ain, I am in vain. People look what you have done! Just take a look.
I   have tried to make the world better. I have tried, I really have, but
     the world is no better.
N   o one will listen but one day they will see and know what I was
     talking about.
G   one, everything's gone, even people are gone. *Danger* is near but
     no one can see it.

Evoyia Linton (11)
Skinners Company School For Girls

LOVE IS . . .

Love is roses falling from the sky
Love is candles lighting up the night
Love is chocolate melting in my mouth
Love is . . .

Love is a big, fluffy cloud
Love is a dream that never ends
Love is you, love is me
Love is . . .

Love is Heaven, but sometimes Hell
Love is never hard to tell
Love is everything I want
Love is you, love is me
Love is . . .

Love is warm and cosy too
Love is bright, but sometimes dark
Love is . . .

Claudia Tumba (13)
Skinners Company School For Girls

TEACHERS WHO JUST DON'T UNDERSTAND

'Why can't you kids just be quiet for one moment?' she yells
Millions of teachers around the world just don't understand
They moan and groan and always complain.

'Take your coats off now!' they scream
They just don't understand that it's too cold
When we ask them for help
They just put us on hold.

You try and hide your chewing gum
But they always notice
You can't get away from them
If you do anything bad they send you to the office.

You don't want to do your homework
They just give you detention
That's just the way teachers are
You're gonna have to put up with them forever and ever.

Sumayya Teladia (13)
Skinners Company School For Girls

GOODNIGHT

So it's time for you to go to sleep
Now you're gone we will all weep
'Cause you were so special to us
You were the one we could always trust.

Those eyes were a bluey-green
When I looked in them it was like a dream
You were so kind and strong
You tried your best to stop things from going wrong.

That's why we love you so very much
Every one of our hearts you touched
So our love for you will never stop
Even if the world went pop.

So goodnight
Sleep tight
And soon we will meet on the other side.

Sophie Mason (13)
Skinners Company School For Girls

HOOKING MRS RIGHT

Women are, women are, women are
Women are strong
Women are pretty
Women are slim, women are soft
Women have friends
Women love to dance
Women drink wine
Women are shy and do show tears
Women shake hands
Women are women and women are gentle
Women don't touch
Women are drips
Women give hugs and kisses
Women hate fighting
Women like cars
Women like gossiping with friends in bingo
Women like shopping
And now and then
Women like, women like, women like women
No they don't
Women care for each other
Women like entertainment
Women are clever and women wear stylish things.

Aminat Salami (13)
Skinners Company School For Girls

WAY OF LIFE

The best way to cheer up yourself
Is to cheer up someone else
The best and most beautiful things in the world
Cannot be seen or even touched
They must be felt with the heart

Dream as if you'll live forever
Live as if you'll die today
Try to learn something about everything
And everything about something
It is never too late to be what you might have been.

Cassie Lucas (13)
Skinners Company School For Girls

MY BEST FRIEND

Sophie is her name
Laughing is her game
Personality, looks, charm
She could never do any harm.

Mairi is my name
Laughing is my game
Personality, looks, charm
I could never do any harm.

As you can see we're two of a kind
Love to us is so blind
We may not be in the right place at the right time
But I know she'll always be mine.

Her smile is like the rising sun
No one could be more fun
Without her my world would end
Together the rules we bend.

I just want her to know
My love for her will never go
Cheerful, loving Sophie
She deserves a trophy.

Mairi McCabe-Williams (14)
Skinners Company School For Girls

THE WRITE STUFF

We start where you start
And end where you end
Sometimes we make sense
Or drive you round the bend
We are neat and clear
Or scruffy and tangled
The ts stand proud
And the ys are dangled
We are present in stories
And open your mind
We can be short and cruel
Or longer and kind
Stand us in a line
Or heap us on a mound
Take a look around
We are everywhere to be found
We march on the paper
Or flit high with the birds
I know you've now guessed it
We're words, words, words!

Shazia-Gul Shahzad (13)
Skinners Company School For Girls

REMEMBRANCE - HOLLY AND JESSICA

D   epression, heartache
E   motions are rising, their tragic death will always be in our memories
A   moment of remembrance, a moment of peace
T   he world is coming to an end, what's going on?
H   elp, peace, they wanted not an early death, but to live and enjoy the
    world, they can no longer see.

Vanessa Ampratwum (11)
Skinners Company School For Girls

THE RIGHT THINGS TO DO IN SCHOOL

O rder in school
B ehaviour in your school
E fficient in school
D iscipline in your school at all times
I ndiscrimination towards others
E at with a knife and fork in the dining hall
N eatly dress for school
T idy in school at all times.
    That's how you should behave at your school.

Donnelia McLarty (12)
Skinners Company School For Girls

THROUGH THE EYES OF A CAT

I rise on my paws and go outside,
It's much colder than I recall,
Soon I have to grow my winter coat.
I stop and stare, it's all so different.
Under my paws I hear the crunch, crunch of leaves,
My cat eyes can't see colour, but the shade of the leaves is different.
Confused by my own domain I go next door,
A leaf is falling from a tree,
Like a bee leaving its hive.
Instinctively I jump at the leaf, but I miss
As I lie there on the bed of decrepit leaves,
I begin to fall asleep, until I hear a shuffling.
I see a small, strange creature trying to hide in a bush,
Mesmerised by it I sit and stare.
It's covered in spikes so I don't try to catch it
Instead I wonder why everything's changed?
I ponder this for a while, until I hear
The rat-a-tat-tat of the food tin and rush back inside.

Sarah Taylor-McAllister (12)
Walthamstow School For Girls

AUTUMN

The leaves fall off trees
And start to flutter
One by one on
The ground.

All the creatures underneath
Begin to shout for
Help to be
Found.

The time goes past and the trees
Go bald all the tree sellers
Get cross they'll
Have to carry
Them back
Unsold.

Najima Issa (11)
Walthamstow School For Girls

DREAMS OF FIRE

Everything is cramped in my head,
I nearly thought I was dead,
All the colours flashing past me,
The hot fire is what I see,
The heat burning under my sole,
I wish it turned cold,
Suddenly the sky turned dark red
And I woke up in my bed.

Saiqa Hawa (11)
Walthamstow School For Girls

MAGGOT

The maggot slowly consumes me,
Meandering through my acquiescent soul,
Creating tunnels of negativity
That collapse in a sludge
Of unrecognisable me

The maggot, gorged on my life essence,
Gravitating to my very core
In its search for new existence,
It flies off to uneaten corruption
Here I lie, the lovely apple shell,
Belying the messy nothingness inside.

Sumbal Khan (14)
Walthamstow School For Girls

DREAMS

Dreams can be bad or good.
They can be adventurous or mysterious.
They can be soft and sweet
Or fast and dangerous.
Dreams can be your command
Or against what you wish.
Sometimes you can't control dreams
But sometimes you think you can.
You can have different types of dreams.
Dreams can be anything you want.

Ceryse Taylor (11)
Walthamstow School For Girls

YOUNG EYES, OLD EYES, MY EYES

Some believe they would never unveil their soul to
                              another human being,
When one look into your eyes is the true soul they're seeing,
They reveal the innermost feelings of the soul
And your personality naked for others to behold.
When you peer into someone's eyes look further than those pearls,
You see the truth and their reaction to the world.
Young eyes wonder and soak in their surroundings,
Absorbing, learning and yearning for more,
The rapture, glamour, the aroma of it all.
But their eyes are impressionable and some desperately search,
To leave the sadness, the poverty, to get away from the hurt.
Such trusting eyes are innocent and see what they want.
Daydreams coming to life
and seek nurturing of older eyes, where their feelings derive.
Behind those lowered eyelids, succeed by the ravages of time,
Lies experience, knowledge, familiarity, warmth and
                              respect of their minds.
My eyes . . . show how I see the world of souls around me.
My eyes see volumes others speak, that express more than
                              voices ever could.
Young and old eyes have their own stories to tell,
Look into my eyes, unlock my heart and bare the soul that
                              endeavours its way into the future.

Kaysea Bonds (14)
Walthamstow School For Girls

GROOVY GREEN

Groovy green is the colour of the grass,
That grows from the ground,
It reminds me of soft, spiky hair growing on my head
And the lawnmower cuts it off.

Groovy green is the colour of the uniform I wear,
That I put on to go to school,
It reminds me of summer trees
And we grow each year.

Claire Woolcott (12)
Walthamstow School For Girls

THE INVISIBLE WALL

Why can't you hear me?
Am I invisible?
Why are you walking past me like I don't exist?
Am I invisible?
Why don't you look at me?
Am I invisible?
Why am I speaking to you and yet you don't even bat an eyelid?
Am I invisible?
Why am I crying inside my heart and you don't even shed a tear?
Am I invisible?
Why is it that a stain is noticed on your coat
But I am merely a speck of dust on your window sill?
Am I invisible?
Why do you never listen to me
Yet expect me to cling on to every word you say?
Am I invisible?
How can you have no feelings for me and yet drown
                              others with affection?
Am I invisible?
Why do you walk right past me and not look back?
Am I invisible?
Jut because you can't hear - doesn't mean I don't have a voice.
To you, I am invisible.

Isabelle Fathimani (15)
Walthamstow School For Girls

GOOD VS EVIL

When I am thinking hard,
I hear a little ticking,
I'm deep into my thoughts,
My tongue is slightly clicking,
I know what is out there,
In the nasty world,
People tricking and fooling around,
Just to get to a little girl,
I often think it's me
They're going to come and get,
I scream in all my nightmares,
I try to never let
Them come and take me away,
I'd missed the people who loved me,
That's only a minority,
Some people never loved me,
I see it in the distance,
The perfect family standing,
I live in a foster home,
But I wish that I was stranded,
I often think my mother
Will think about coming back,
She'd kiss me and she'd hug me,
Then hide me in a sack,
I know it's mad to think this,
I know she'll never come,
But imagination sometimes helps,
Especially when evil's won.

Danielle Ferguson (14)
Walthamstow School For Girls

WORM ON A BUILDING SITE

The darkness always packed in around me
A soft cushion of dirt enveloping me
I never wanted to learn, to be taught
Any answers will sink away through my damp bed of earth
But rumbles break through this black nothing
So far away it can only confuse me
I know it's coming closer and a strange feeling
So cold and yet burning, because I'm afraid.

All quaking around, I can't hold tight
In kind earth. In loose soil I'm tumbled
And air washes over me. Cool, painfully fresh
Too new for any thought, but I am free
And I see now. All so strange and light
I never could dream this to be real
So many grey blocks and green, curving horizons
And above. Such a blue. An unreachable blue
I am lifting, lifting. So distant from everything
I know. But I grow strong every moment I rise
Now where nothing could be true, I see a world.

I have no arms to stretch in this waking. No legs to dance
Oh! But I will grow legs now
And I will walk in great, striding steps across this earth
I know now it all can be mine. I will own while I still see
So now I fall back, rushing down to beautiful power
Claiming what I long for, what is given to me.

It hits the ground, feeling earth beneath it again
Burrowing, so desperately back to sweet, chilled dirt . . . bliss
All is forgotten

No cares for a worm in a building site of diggers.

Ellen Buddle (15)
Walthamstow School For Girls

MYSTERIOUS FOREST

As a ribbon of darkness sweeps the land,
You hear the sound of a music band
And all the ghosts and ghouls step out of the trees,
With chains round their ankles and upon their knees,
They play battered drums
And wooden flutes,
The ghouls are wearing moth-eaten suits,
The ghosts are wearing dirty rags
And the ladies have even got mouldy handbags.

They play and play,
Until it is day,
Which is time for them to go away,
Back through the trees
And mass of bushes,
In which when they pass,
It rustles and brushes,
Up comes the sun,
After the red, glowing dawn,
Bird sing to greet the early morn.

Clare Green (11)
Walthamstow School For Girls

DREAMS

D   reams come at night, sometimes give you a horrible fright,
R   ealistic ones are what I like,
E   lephants or other animals don't have dreams,
A   ll they do is confuse you,
M   agic dreams are what kids believe,
S   o they think dreams come true.

Anum Saghir (11)
Walthamstow School For Girls

MY DREAMY DAY

Last time I dreamed I won a million pounds
for just lying in my bed,
but then my mum said, 'Wake up!'
So when I was at school I went
into a daydream about what I would buy,
clothes, trainers, shoes, houses, CDs, chocolate,
and maybe some strawberry lace
but then my teacher shouted, 'Get out your pencil case!'
I was off school, whoo!
It was like a dream come true
the hours went quick
time for bed
so have a nice dream.

Sophie Cavill (11)
Walthamstow School For Girls

DREAMS

C   ranky dreams are really wacky
R   eally cool or really tacky
A   bsurd dreams are very
Z   any
Y   es, dreams are really crazy!

D   reams really can come true,
R   elaxing ones, scary ones, or those that bode fortune for you
E   veryone's dreams are different we know
A   nd most dreams very swiftly vanish and go. But
M   any are memorable and their images last
S   o it's my future I'm wobbly about and not my past!

Jessica Collins (11)
Walthamstow School For Girls

CANDYFLOSS PINK

Candyfloss pink is a designer T-shirt waiting for me to buy.
Candyfloss pink is the colour of my favourite pen and hairbands,
that are girlie and cute.
Candyfloss pink is the colour of the sticky funfair food.
Candyfloss pink is the colour of hearts and anything fluffy.
Candyfloss pink is the strawberry ice cream
with lots of sauce and sprinkles.

Georgia-Kate Hepting (11)
Walthamstow School For Girls

BLAZIN' BLUE

Blazin' blue is the colour of the sky on a hot summer's day,
It is the colour of most of the leisure clothes in my wardrobe,
It is the colour of the water we drink, the sea we swim in
and the colour of our veins.
It is the colour of the ink we write with and the colour of Tesco,
Blazin' blue is a calm, cool, refreshing colour and it's my favourite.

Naomi Hutchinson (11)
Walthamstow School For Girls

SUMMER - LIGHT YELLOW

Summer - light yellow is the colour of the sun,
Umbrellas that are needed on the rainiest days
Of the sand on the sandiest beach
And a part of the rainbow that comes in different ways.
Summer - light yellow is the colour of the happiest times
For everyone and the colour of you and me.

Emma Fisher (11)
Walthamstow School For Girls

AUTUMN

Autumn's here, when the green, glistening leaves,
Start growing out of the tree.
Autumn's here, when the green, juicy apples,
Stop growing and fall out of the tree.
It's here, it's here, now there's play and joy,
Oh yes, it's my birthday I can't wait to get a toy.
Autumn's here when the great big plums
Fall down. I catch it, soggy, but *yum!*

Nosheen Tabsim (11)
Walthamstow School For Girls

MY FAVOURITE COLOUR - BLUE

Blue is the colour of the ocean, which I call ocean blue.
Blue is the colour of the morning and night sky.
Blue is the fourth colour in a rainbow.
The colour blue shows shy, sad or even lonely.
Guess which one I am?
Guess why my favourite colour is blue?

Anisha Rambojun (11)
Walthamstow School For Girls

COOL BLUE

Cool blue reminds me of the sun shining
On the swimming pool as I swim in the cool breeze.
A hot summer's day with light blue sky.
Blue is one of my favourite colours.

Khadisha Gerald (11)
Walthamstow School For Girls

LOVE/HATE

I love him, I hate him.
I care for him, yet disregard him.
I'd crave to see his happy smile and lack seeing his scary snarl.
I want to be near and so, so far.
I want to feel his lovely long hair and give him a haircut.
I love/hate.

Sangeeta Ramalingam (12)
Walthamstow School For Girls

AUTUMN LEAVES

Autumn is a bad time for leaves,
Autumn leaves sink down from the trees,
Down they float like beautiful, fluttering butterflies,
Swirling on the ground they look wonderful,
Crunch!
The leaf is in tiny, crunched pieces.

Uzma Sajid (11)
Walthamstow School For Girls

WHAT IS A DREAM?

A dream is a piece of falsehood
a story swishing through your head.
Whenever you sleep the word
dream whispers in your ear.

Dreamy dreams make you fall asleep
you just want to stay in your dream in peace and harmony.
When it's morning you don't want to eat
you just want to go back to sleep.

Dreams come at night,
they sometimes give you a big nasty fright.
Make your dream happy or sad
otherwise you might be living in an old bag.

Dreams are fun, dreams are happy
some are sad and some are bad,
so that is that.
A dream is just a dream.

Atia Raja (11)
Walthamstow School For Girls

DREAMS

D ream all day, dream all night,
R aaaah! Maybe they will give you a fright.
E nd the dream with a happy rhyme,
A nd then don't think about your dream in daytime,
M ake your dream come true,
S o maybe you might end up seeing the Blazin' Squad crew.

Farva Butt (11)
Walthamstow School For Girls

DREAMS

Dreams, dreams, what a wonderful thing
I could dream all day that's my thing
I could dream all night
I wish I never see daylight
In a dream anything can happen
When you dream your imagination's open.

Wajiha Dadabhoy (11)
Walthamstow School For Girls

DREAMS

D ark mysterious dreams that keep you thinking.
R epeating dreams that you have again and again.
E xtraordinary weird dreams that leave you confused.
A ction dreams that leave you excited.
M agic dreams that you usually forget.
S cary dreams that leave you frightened.
   All types of dreams!

Leah Hajowyj (11)
Walthamstow School For Girls

DREAMS

D is for dreams never to be told
R is for revolting disadvantages in dreams
E is for edible dreams
A is for amazing never-ending dreams
M is for misfortune, never to happen again
S is for surreal dream-like dreams.

Shana Beharry-Stroude (11)
Walthamstow School For Girls

THE DANCING WIND

Dreaming, dreaming, the dream of the wind
The wind was as strong as a giant,
It was as cool as an ice cream
Sweeping up the leaves. The wind was dancing, dancing.

The wind was as breezy as a fan
Blow my clothes up and down
The wind gave me a cold chill,
The wind was dancing, dancing.

The wind was howling like a ghost,
It whizzed around me like a bee
Trying to scare me away
The wind was dancing, dancing.

Kara Sewell (11)
Walthamstow School For Girls

AUTUMN

Millions of reds and browns, oranges and greens.
Falling into a whirlwind of wind and rain.
Seasons happen again and again and again.
Autumn is my favourite season
As I read this poem I shall tell you my reason.
Autumn is so colourful and bright
Gloomy, dark and rainy it is filled with light.
Even though it pours with rain
My heart stays the very same.

Naomi Ackie (11)
Walthamstow School For Girls

AUTUMN LEAVES

Crunch, crunch is the sound as I trudge through the fallen leaves,
I know that autumn has finally arrived,
The leaves have turned copper brown colours,
Together leaves flutter down towards the ground,
They are like zooming aeroplanes coming to land,
Crackling is all I hear apart from the sound
of the cold autumn breeze, rustling in the trees.
Change is all around now; soon winter takes over.

Jessica Meredeen (11)
Walthamstow School For Girls

AT NIGHT . . .

At night I heard the strangest things which cannot be explained
And when I switched on the light all my fears were drained.
I switch off the light and there it is walking to me now,
This creature must live from the dark, I don't understand how.
I saw this creature take flight, it flew past me, but didn't bite
It flew out the window, gone forever
Will it come back? No - never!

Humaa Kazim (12)
Walthamstow School For Girls

DOLPHIN BLUE

Dolphin blue is the colour
of the sea and dolphins.
It reminds me of the sea
swishing and swoshing.
It is like the vein
which runs through me
and also is a part of me.

Sophia Yousaf (11)
Walthamstow School For Girls

AUTUMN

It's autumn and the leaves are falling silently on to the ground.
Red, brown, yellow and green are there to be found.
Crinch, crunch I hear as I walk passed the bare trees,
People shiver and quickly open doors with their keys.
Tomorrow the leaves will be gone
Because it will be winter and autumn will be gone.

Shafiqah Amiji (11)
Walthamstow School For Girls

THE BUTTERCUP

Buttercup is the colour of a hot sun and is the colour of a daffodil.
Buttercup reminds me of when I went to Mauritius
because the country is very hot.
Buttercup is like a yellow autumn leaf falling to the muddy ground.
The colour of buttercup also reminds me of people being in a
grateful, generous or even good mood.
The becoming colour of the buttercup coming towards me
and the smell follows my hand as they are trying to grab it
but suddenly it has already gone (the smell) up my nose.

Faheza Noorkhan (11)
Walthamstow School For Girls

SEA-BLUE

Sea-blue is the colour of the sea
It reminds me of swimming in the Jamaican sea
When I see sky-blue it reminds me of the sea.

Warm, sparkling in the sun, waves splashing against my face
In the sand hide sand crabs, they bite my feet.

Sherona Bailey (11)
Walthamstow School For Girls

DOLPHIN BLUE

Dolphin blue reminds me of the night-blue sky.
It also reminds me of a lonely mood
Dolphin blue reminds me of different shades of blue
from the lightest to darkest
Different shades of blue are loved by nearly everyone.

Charelle Walton (11)
Walthamstow School For Girls

FANTASY DREAMS

Fishes ate flying in the sky,
The birds ate eating pie.

The river is flowing in the sky,
The mold is swimming in the pool.

The doll is chasing me with a knife
And I am running for my life.

The turtle and the rabbit are racing
And the cows are dancing on the moon.

The mice are singing on the clouds
And the hands are eating gum.

The teddy bears are humming
And the frogs are chatting.

Mehreen Butt (11)
Walthamstow School For Girls

LOOPY LASS

When it comes to loopiness
She's right top of the class,
She's utterly loopy, monsterly scatty,
Mentally wacky, totally funky,
Wild and crazy,
Fantastic and funky,
She's the gorgeous, loopy lass!

Tajmin Choudhury (12)
Walthamstow School For Girls

AUTUMN

Red, green and gold
Flowing, dying
Leaves dance in the sunshine
Flowing down, down in the moonlight
Just as the forest wakes
Nothing can be heard.

Crinkle, crackle, crack and crunch
Sun looking in through the forest tops between the trees
Green, dark greens
Now reds, oranges and browns.

As fairies dance in the last bright sunlight
Leaves flow down in the darkness.
Autumn is here!

Karen Black (11)
Walthamstow School For Girls

DREAMS

What is a dream?
A dream can be anything
You want it to be.
A dream can be real
Or as adventurous as you want it to be.
A dream can give you a fright.
You may or may not remember it
But always remember you will have an effect.

Mariam Malik (12)
Walthamstow School For Girls

MY DREAMS

Fantastical and mythical but sometimes mundane,
Magical and meaningful are all senses in my dreams,
But your dreams might not seem as you imagine it.

Exciting and happy dreams make me feel special,
However, frightening and sad dreams make me feel trapped,
As you dream through the night, your dreams mix up
And in the morning they are gone.

When a nightmare takes me, I wake with a jolt,
Not knowing where I am is puzzling and confusing,
Soon the eerie memory leaves me and I find
Myself cosy and warm in my own bed.

Rachel Meredeen (11)
Walthamstow School For Girls

DREAM POEM

There are many dreams to write about,
although you may be scared.
There are many dreams when you scream and shout,
although they may be weird.

There are many dreams to say and see,
although you may be sad.
There are many dreams with you and me,
although you might feel mad.

Tobi Adewale (11)
Walthamstow School For Girls

DREAMS

Dreams come in all different shapes and sizes,
Some are long and boring.
Others are quick and over in a second.
Some have colours and sound,
Some dreams are black and white,
No wonder you have them
    in
       the
          middle of
            the
               night

Dreams come as feelings or people that you love,
Some are sad and lonely,
In others you're laughing and happy.
Some are frightening like nightmares,
Or you're watching a light,
No wonder you have them
    in
       the
          middle of
            the
               night.

Hannah Cheston (11)
Walthamstow School For Girls